30 DAYS TO

Thriving

PRACTICAL INSPIRATION FOR RECLAIMING YOUR HOPE & HEALTH

— JENNIFER ZIMMER —

GOLDENPEN MEDIA
REDEEMING HOPE, REVEALING GOLD.

30 DAYS TO THRIVING

Practical Inspiration for Reclaiming Your Hope & Health
By Jennifer Zimmer

ISBN: 978-0-9994383-0-5
Library of Congress Control Number: 2017917538
GoldenPen Media, Redding, CA

Edited by Kim Julian & Peggy Stovesand
Cover Design by Linda Lee
Layout by Jonathan McGraw
Bio Photograph by Jack Vu

For permission requests, write to the publisher at the address below:
GoldenPen Media
PO Box 493462
Redding, California/96002

www.jenniferzimmer.com

• • •

*"Life isn't about waiting for the storm to pass...
it's about learning to dance in the rain."*

VIVIAN GREENE

DEDICATION

...

This book is dedicated to the memory of my late husband,

Peter Lloyd Johnston

Through his life he taught me to live beyond my comfort zone, to take giant leaps of faith, and always follow my heart. Without his enthusiastic support, I likely never would have attempted to begin writing this book. Peter lived life with a rare level of excellence, faith, and integrity, always encouraging me to apply those same qualities to my open and honest writing. I've done my best to honor him in that. He is missed every single day, but will always be alive with us in our hearts.

This book is also dedicated to my loving husband,

Lance Wade Zimmer

Through your genuine kindness, compassion, and friendship, you cheered Peter and I on in hopes of seeing redemption unfold for our family. And when we suddenly lost Peter, you were there to listen, to encourage, and to laugh with me even when I didn't think I could laugh anymore. In you I found a kindred spirit, an unexpected second chance at love. This book surely would not have become a reality if not for your unwavering support. Thank you for believing in me. I love you always and forever.

PREFACE
A Disclaimer

• • •

Within the pages of this book you will find a window into my personal journey through trauma and loss. It cannot be ignored that my late husband, Peter, plays a key role in my story. After all, he was my life partner for over sixteen years and his struggles were also my struggles. As Ann Voscamp states in her book *The Broken Way,* "Hurt is a contagion. When one person hurts in a family, everyone aches."

All that Peter and I walked through together provided me with the experiences that led to the writing of this book. We were different in many ways, but one thing that we had in common was that we both chose to live transparent lives. We were as open about our victories as we were about our battles. So it came as no surprise to me that he also chose to be open about the great challenges he faced during the last four years of his life.

It was in May of 2014 that I approached Peter with my concern for his privacy as I had begun writing this book. We were nearing the end of our divorce process for the second time at this point, although it was never what I wanted. To say that our situation was complicated is an enormous understatement. How could I explain to anyone how much we loved each other yet how necessary it had become for us to separate? It was out of my genuine love and concern for Peter that I walked into his home office on that day in May and presented a question to him.

You know I'm writing my book now and I'm wondering if you'd feel more comfortable with me writing as Jennifer Cannon to protect your identity? Our divorce will be final by the time this book comes out and I don't need to use the name Johnston if you'd prefer that I don't. I can't remove you from my story, but I can try to cover you if you'd prefer that.

I still remember the way he stopped what he was doing, spun around in his office chair and looked at me straight in the eye as he delivered his true-to-character response.

Jen, this is your story and you need to tell it. I want you to tell it. I'm an open book, so you can say whatever you want. I have nothing to hide. You have my full permission to share our story.

This is exactly the response I would have expected from him. There was more that he shared with me, words I will forever cherish, but I will save that for another time. His verbal release became even more of a gift to me when, less than one week later, Peter was suddenly gone from our lives forever.

I understand that some of what you will read in these pages could be perceived as dishonoring to Peter or the life that we shared together. But that is not my heart. On the contrary, what I share with you in this book is intended to honor his life and the incredible man that he was. It is my wish not to expose him, but instead to reveal how he and I both suffered as a result of his unrelenting affliction, the affliction that would later take him from this earth completely. And I do so with his full permission.

While I considered giving up on this book project more than once, I couldn't let it go in good conscience. I don't want Peter's battle, nor my own, to be in vain. I simply cannot forget what we walked through and the world of pain that was opened up to me as a result. There are more people than we realize who suffer in the shadows, too afraid, ashamed or just plain too tired to ask for help. If this describes you, nothing would bless me more than to know that this book has made it into your hands. I pray that my transparency reaches out to you across the pages and that you'll find comfort in knowing that you're not alone.

CONTENTS

SECTION 3: MEET MY THRIVING FRIENDS

INTRODUCTION
A Letter to My Readers

· · ·

Dear Friend,

Welcome! I want to begin by sharing my heart for you, my reader, and what I hope you will gain from this book. Now I realize that you may be reading this book not because you're immediately in need of what I have to offer, but perhaps you know me personally or you know someone who does. To you I say thank you! Thank you for reading, thank you for your support, and thank you for sharing this book with your friends and acquaintances.

If your life is super, then great! You probably know someone who could use a healthy dose of hope, so please consider passing this book along to them. There comes a time for all of us when we can benefit from practical coping strategies to get through a trying season of life. And when that time comes, I hope that you'll recall the stories and tools I have to share and be strengthened and encouraged by them.

For those of you who currently feel a more urgent need for support in your life, I can't tell you how happy it makes me that you're here. You have been in my heart and prayers for quite a long time. Even as I write this, I close my eyes and imagine you holding this book. I feel *so* proud of you.

You might not feel like a thriving survivor right now, but you are that and so much more. My wish is that I could look you in the eye, tell you that you're going to be okay and give you the kind of hug that penetrates deep into your heart. You *will* be okay, my friend. I'm in this with you. What you're going through now isn't going to last forever.

I may not know the details of your journey, but I do know what it feels like to be in a distressing season of life that you didn't necessarily sign up for. Feeling like I'd barely survived a shipwreck, I recall wondering whether I'd ever make it ashore. The swim to get there felt impossible as all my strength had been exhausted in the process of enduring each day.

For a time, I actually believed that I wouldn't make it. In fact, I was convinced that I was dying. The battle had been too fierce and my body was failing me in mysterious and scary ways that no doctor was able to resolve. I wept in deep despair, prematurely grieving the years that I wouldn't be around to see my children grow up. It does seem so silly now, but it felt all too real to me at the time.

As you may have experienced yourself, I lost my hope along with my health. It seems that the two often times go hand in hand. The reality of continuing to live day in and day out through my own personal nightmare felt like too great of a burden to bear. All I wanted to do was wake up and find that none of it was real after all, but rather a bad dream. I so badly wanted to go back to my happy life, the life I enjoyed before the unwelcome anguish invaded our world.

Watching others enjoy their seemingly trouble-free lives through the lens of social media, I sometimes felt angry. How dare they be so carefree, out and about having a great time while I remained chained to this misery with no hope of escape in the foreseeable future? It felt like no one could understand my pain. I felt isolated and restricted to my very small world where survival was the goal most days.

Once I discovered and implemented a few simple tools, it wasn't long at all before I was back on my feet. My circumstances didn't change, but I certainly did. The nightmare continued to swirl around me, but I was safe in the eye of the storm. Not only was I safe, but also I was truly happy. I was living a life that I never would have lived had I not been pushed to the end of myself.

What about you? Where do you find yourself today? Has your hope faded away? Do you feel paralyzed by despair? Is the stress of your situation causing your health to fail? If so, rest assured there *is* a way through this. I've written this book just for you and others like you because I feel completely confident that you'll be well on your way to the thriving life you've been longing for in as little as thirty days. Hope and health are not as far off as they may seem.

I understand that this trial you're facing now may feel like a curse. But let me suggest to you that wrapped up in all of the turmoil is an unexpected gift. Believe it or not, this gift is already being made manifest in you. You've made it this far because you're stronger than you know. And there is yet more strength to be found in the days ahead. My trials have a way of forging a new me that never would have surfaced if not subjected to great pressure. Your trials can do the same for you!

You see, my friend, you have available to you everything you need to not just make it through, but to uncover a version of yourself that will astound you. It *is* possible to thrive despite your circumstances, I promise! I'm here to walk you through this, to cheer you on. I'm going to provide you with some practical tools to shift your course until you finally reclaim your hope and health. I have written this book of personal transformation as a daily guide for you to take your first steps towards a new and wonderful life.

It's the little choices throughout each day that will get you to where you want to be. If you put these tools into practice, at the end of thirty days you'll look back and discover how far you've come. Your joy will be restored. Your strength will be renewed. Good health will be on its way. You'll be thriving in areas you didn't imagine possible. And you'll think about your tomorrows without fear, but rather with hopeful anticipation. *You. Will. Overcome.*

Your comrade in this journey,

Jennifer Zimmer

Section ONE

• • •

MY PATH TO
THRIVING

Chapter One

TRAUMA IN PARADISE

• • •

Have you ever experienced a day that changed your life forever? A wedding. The birth of your first child. The loss of a loved one. A major move to a new place. Or perhaps you walked through an open door one day that changed the course of your life in some drastic way. This is the expected and normal stuff of life.

Most of our days are lived in between these peaks and valleys. Sometimes we know in advance when a defining moment is approaching and, at other times, it catches us completely off-guard. Maybe we didn't see it coming. Or maybe we just never thought *that* could happen to *us*. But those unexpected, altogether unwelcome surprises *do* happen in life. And that's what happened to me.

JUNE 29, 2010: PETER'S 35TH BIRTHDAY

Our eighteen-year-old son, Mark, had recently graduated from Kohala High School and gave us a mere three-day warning that he would be leaving the nest. He was determined to return to our previous home in Mammoth Lakes, California where a good portion of our family still resided. And this was it—moving day. He was flying to the mainland on Peter's birthday.

Mark wasn't happy in Hawaii and tensions between us had been running high. Even still, my mama's heart was feeling torn in two. I wasn't ready to see him go. We would soon have an ocean between us and that ocean had never felt so vast. But he was a legal adult now and this was his decision.

While Mark packed up his belongings for the big move, Peter spent most of his birthday downstairs in his man cave below the kitchen. He seemed to be a bit emotional, but then again so was I. As I went about my day, I could hear him playing his guitar, singing, and sometimes laughing. This was not at all abnormal for Peter who often spent the bulk of his days getting lost in his own music.

At the time, we were at a sort of high point in our financial lives after selling a successful business that we'd started back in Mammoth. We were completely debt-free with a healthy nest egg in reserves. Peter continued to work part-time from his home office in Kapa'au, but only as much as necessary. The majority of his time was spent creating.

At his core, Peter was primarily a musician and a worshipper. He had turned his man cave in the garage into a sort of holy space where he would sing his heart out to God. There was no lack of passion in that man, which was evident in his expressive songs. Actually, it was evident in just about everything Peter did.

At some point on this particular day, I began to hear a less familiar sound. Weeping. The sound of dramatic weeping seeped through the kitchen floor from the garage below. I knew that we were feeling the angst of Mark leaving us, but it wasn't like Peter to manifest such strong emotions in this way. I proceeded down our steep staircase to the garage to investigate.

There I found my six-foot-five husband lying on the red rug below his desk. And he was weeping. And laughing. And carrying on about spiritual things that I couldn't quite piece together. He kept saying, "I believe, I believe!" He seemed happy, almost drunk in fact. I just sat and watched for awhile, not sure about what to make of his behavior. Did this have something to do with Mark leaving?

Coming from what some might call a wild Pentecostal upbringing, it wasn't completely foreign to me to see a person in this state. Someone having an encounter with the presence of God might look a little like Peter did there on the garage floor. I decided that maybe this was some kind of a divine encounter he was having, a gift from the Father on Peter's birthday perhaps.

I took out my camera and began to record a video of Peter who only persisted with the crying and the laughing. Like any good laughter, it was contagious and I began to join in with him. I posted a clip of the video I took on social media with a caption about Peter being blessed on his birthday. Friends who saw the video seemed to agree with me that he was having some kind of an inexplicable spiritual encounter.

The crying continued and I became less and less amused by it. Peter's red eyes swelled, highlighting his bright blue irises. My concern grew as he seemed to be unable to turn off this highly emotional state he was in. It came out that his encounter had something to do with a song he was writing called *The Master Plan,* a song that can still be found on YouTube.

Somehow we managed to pull ourselves together enough to make the hour-long drive to Kona to see Mark off at the airport. From the time we said our good-byes and got back into our '95 Land Cruiser, we cried all the way home. Our remaining young children, ages one, three and six at the time, were heartbroken to see their older brother go.

We had adopted Mark when he was nine years old, but his presence in our family was all our younger children had ever known. Through his sweet tears, our six-year-old son, Alex, decided that he would never turn eighteen and leave us. And that was just fine with me.

Once we returned home, Peter didn't rest. He set about the work of detailing Mark's room and sorting through the remnants that were left behind. Peter was a driven, goal-oriented person who never met a project that intimidated him. He didn't stop until the job was done and done well, which I was glad for most of the time.

As Peter worked downstairs in Mark's room, he continued to sing as though he was somewhere else. This was not out of character for him. He was known for having his head in the clouds. This was evident from the time we first met in college as a friend gifted Peter with a lamp topped by a cloud shade. "It reminded me of you," they had said.

All of the emotions of our eventful day did finally catch up to Peter and he turned in for the night before nine o'clock. But about four hours later, he was awake and feeling stirred deeply. Sleep escaped him as this new high he was on seemed to carry him away to a place that I didn't understand. His eyes were wide with wonder and he laughed at the apparent revelation that was flooding his spirit.

Over the course of the next week, my uneasiness only grew as Peter's behavior became increasingly bizarre. I would find things in very unusual places after he had unloaded the dishwasher. He *knew* where those things went and never had a problem with this task before. When I pointed out what he had done, he seemed to be as baffled as I was.

Peter possessed a gift I envied where sleep was concerned. Normally, he would be sound asleep in less than sixty seconds after his head hit the pillow. But now, sleep evaded him, as did his appetite. His weight was dropping and his activity level was increasing. I soon knew in my gut that something was very wrong.

In sharing my concerns with family, it seemed that the idea that Peter was having an inexplicable spiritual encounter was easier to embrace than the frightening physical alternatives. I didn't know what to think, honestly. I only knew something was off and my husband was not himself.

After about a week, Peter's peculiar behavior seemed to fade away. I was relieved and eager for a break from my post as constant husband observer. But the break was short-lived, unfortunately, as an uncharacteristic demeanor seemed to fall over Peter again a few weeks later. This time, however, it showed up with a vengeance and I was terrified.

AUGUST 1, 2010: ALEX'S 7TH BIRTHDAY

I'll save the full story of what Peter and I called "episode two" for another day, perhaps another book. What I will tell you is that on August first, Alex's seventh birthday, all hell broke loose. I could no longer keep Peter's confusion a secret.

My concerns about Peter had been kept quiet among my island friends up to this point, but now I had to let them in on exactly what was going on. I couldn't think of inviting people into our home while my shirtless husband was behaving like a mad man, pacing in circles under the scorching sun in our backyard with no regard for the resulting sunburn. It didn't matter that Alex's half-finished birthday cake sat waiting for me on the kitchen counter; his party would have to be postponed. I sent a text out and called the party off with a brief explanation.

As soon as the word was out, friends appeared within minutes. A few of the guys who came by observed Peter in the backyard. One of them paced in circles with him. Some just watched and prayed, as unsure of what to do as I was. None of us had seen anything like this before.

My girlfriends also came to the rescue of Alex's birthday, snatching up his unfinished cake along with the party food from the fridge and whisking it all away. Soon my three children were also gone. I'm thankful for that to this day because they likely would have been severely traumatized by all that followed. Again, a story for another day.

By evening, after a frightening day full of confusion and downright terror, Peter was escorted by two brave male friends to the emergency room a half-hour away. Alex's party was seamlessly salvaged by dear friends who have my heart forever.

When I was finally able to show up at the party, I was greeted by a marching line of camo-clad children who were just returning from an exciting pig hunt in the nearby ravine. They were carrying various weapons and talking wildly about the fun they'd had. Together we watched Alex blow out his candles and make a wish. We enjoyed the chocolate cake while sitting on the ocean view lanai of my friends' rural home. For a moment, it seemed as if nothing at all could possibly be wrong in the world.

Stepping into a quiet corner of my friend's home, I answered a call from the emergency room physician. Through the line, I could hear Peter screaming in the background. The sound of his hysterical voice hit me straight in the gut. It was then that I cried for the first time that day. This was really happening. My husband was suffering terribly and I felt powerless to make it stop.

I explained Peter's recent behavior to the physician, including the part where he was putting things away in strange places. I requested a brain scan. Surely this would provide us with an explanation for it all.

You know you're having a bad day when you find yourself hoping that your husband has a brain tumor, right?

A brain tumor would have been something we could see, something we could treat. A brain tumor would make sense. At this point, I was longing for *anything* to make sense. I'm a solutions kind of girl and I was ready to chase after whatever we needed to do to bring my husband back. I desperately wanted a tangible problem with equally tangible solutions.

Alas, the brain scan was clear. No abnormalities were found. And with no apparent physical ailment to treat, the only course of action to be taken now was a decision made by the ER staff. Peter was placed on an involuntary hold and transferred to a mental health facility in Kona, now an hour away from home.

The diagnosis came the following day: Bipolar Disorder Type 1, first episode. Initially, I scoffed at this supposed diagnosis. Clearly these medically trained people were ignorant. They were unable to recognize a spiritual attack such as the one that had been unleashed upon my husband. I would show them. I would figure this whole thing out and, together, Peter and I would prove them wrong. Or so I thought.

Due to Peter's state of confusion, he told both the authorities and the medical staff that he and I were divorced. As a result, I was unable to speak with him or receive any information about his care. Knowing that he was being kept on a seventy-two-hour hold, I collaborated with Paul, our friend and business partner in Kona, and also Peter's father, John, to formulate a plan. At the end of the three-day hold, I drove down to Kona where Paul and I went together to wait outside of the mental health facility for Peter's anticipated release.

Thankfully he walked out of the hospital at the expected time, laughing and waving the piece of paper detailing his diagnosis like a white flag. Paul and I worked together to keep Peter entertained over lunch as we killed time waiting for my father-in-law to arrive from California. This intervention plan of ours was both nerve-wracking and comical. We knew that things could go terribly wrong at any moment, yet I had to laugh at the hilarity of the situation as Paul and I employed every stall tactic we could think of to keep Peter from doing something that could foil our plan.

I'd never in my life felt so relieved to see John as I was when he at last made a "surprise appearance" at our lunch with Peter. Thanks to him, our intervention was successful and Peter was safely escorted back to California by his father. My mom also flew out from California to help me with the kids during this time. Once Peter was settled in with his parents and receiving care in Mammoth Lakes, my mom watched over my kids while I prepared our family for a potentially lengthy hiatus from our life in Hawaii.

NOVEMBER 2010: MY 36TH BIRTHDAY
+ AN UNEXPECTED MOVE

Following a nearly three-month stay back in California to recuperate from all we'd been through in August, we were ready to resume our life back in Kohala. Peter hadn't seemed to exhibit any of the symptoms we'd seen during his episodes in Hawaii, so we felt like it was time to go home. Perhaps this nightmare was behind us for good.

Unfortunately, Peter's confusion began again within a few days of our return to Kohala at the end of October. (I'll talk a little more about this in a later chapter.) I soon made the heartbreaking decision to move back to California to be closer to family and necessary resources for Peter, but it didn't seem like we could get there fast enough. Peter's situation was escalating quickly. Thankfully I was able to call upon Peter's dad for help once again. He agreed to fly out to be with Peter and travel with him back to California. Although we experienced a considerable amount of stress as we waited for Peter's dad to arrive, I was greatly relieved when their plane at last departed for the mainland on what happened to be my birthday.

A couple of my dear friends threw the sweetest little surprise party for me that evening in Kohala along with all of our young children. There's nothing quite like the feeling of being able to sit among friends who you can be completely real with. They knew I'd been through hell over the past week or so, but they didn't want to pass up an opportunity to celebrate my birthday. I was completely exhausted and did little more than sit on the couch, but I soaked up their love and much-needed comfort. Knowing Peter was in safe hands with his dad helped me to relax a little, but I still felt the uncertainty of our future looming over me.

It wasn't until the day before Thanksgiving that our family was at last reunited in California. Completing the transoceanic moving process without Peter was grueling, but we got through it. Together we took up residence in my hometown of Redding, California. I had made the difficult choice to give up our beautiful life on the Big Island thinking it would only be for a little while. For now, we needed the support of our family and friends in California. Hawaii would still be there when this was all over.

My new mission in life was to do whatever it took to bring the man I had known and loved for over fourteen years back to us. I couldn't possibly fathom a life without him and the idea that he might never recover was more than I could even begin to accept. But was Peter's complete recovery even still attainable? Would he even be capable of cooperating in his own healing? I wasn't so sure. All I knew to do was hope and pray for a miracle.

THE AFTERMATH

In the months and years that would follow, we enjoyed short seasons of calm followed by wave after wave of violent waters. I no longer recognized the man I attempted to have a life with. Peter's torment had forced us out of our beloved life on the island and into a life I never dreamed of. It was not at all what I wanted.

Although I had a few well-meaning friends counsel me to leave him, I wouldn't abandon my husband. I made a vow to Peter to stand by his side in sickness and in health and I was not about to break that vow. It wasn't even an option in my mind. There was no escaping this new unwelcome reality I found myself in.

Living in Redding had never been a part of our plan. I left home for college in the fall of 1995, met Peter five months later and never looked back. Our adventurous life together had led us to live in a number of beautiful places. We were blessed in that way. Now here I was, sixteen years later, suddenly transplanted back to a city that felt like a strange mixture of both familiar and foreign.

Sure, I knew a lot of people. And a lot of people knew me. When I made the decision to move to Redding, I had imagined myself swimming to a shore that would be full of people cheering me on, ready to receive our battered lives and love us back to wholeness. But that wasn't the case. Everyone was apparently so consumed with their own lives that our presence seemed to go almost unnoticed and our crisis was all but completely forgotten. I felt both lost and invisible in my own hometown.

That first year in Redding felt like a death to me. I grieved the loss of our life in Hawaii every single day. I grieved the dreams and prophetic promises that were abandoned. Never had I experienced such an unjust disruption in my life. My heart was legitimately broken and the rest of me soon began to follow.

As I continued to ride the monthly waves of Peter's manic episodes, I felt like I was barely able to come up for air before we were back in crisis mode again. I had become the primary caretaker of not only our three young children at home, but also of my husband whose bipolar episodes had now fallen into a regular monthly pattern that we jokingly dubbed his "manstrual cycle."

Peter wasn't able to focus well enough to work very much. His normally vibrant personality had fallen flat, likely from the medication he was on. The unpredictability of his illness meant that I was constantly vigilant and on guard. Subconsciously, I went about my days bracing myself for whatever trauma might come next. And, inevitably, it would come every single month in varying degrees of severity. After about two years of this, the ongoing stress and trauma became more than I could physically endure.

CRASH AND TURN

...

The ruthless storm that had overtaken our lives at last took a serious toll on my tired body. I would later learn that stress hits us right in the gut, which made complete sense because that's precisely what happened to me. My digestive system was on the fritz. Certain foods couldn't be tolerated at all, like eggs or chocolate *(wince)*. If I ate either one, it was pretty much guaranteed to show up again soon in a partially digested form.

Prior to moving to Hawaii, I had begun working with a naturopathic physician by the name of Dr. Ronda Nelson. I called her in a last-ditch effort to avoid going under the knife as I had a surgeon eager to remove my gallbladder. She quickly responded to my call and, in true Dr. Ronda form, confidently stated, "You can have your gallbladder taken out if you want to. But if you decide you want to keep your body parts, I can help you do that." And that's exactly what she did. It's been ten years and I still have my gallbladder, thanks to her help.

Through our time working together, Dr. Ronda won my trust. She supported me in making many changes in my life, which included giving up gluten. (This could be another book in and of itself, but for now I'll just say that going gluten-free completely changed my life in ways I never thought possible.) Health challenges I'd faced most of my life were dropping off one by one. I was quickly becoming the most healthy version of myself I'd ever been right around the time that Peter became ill.

THE CRASH

Now here I was feeling unwell again. Determined not to sink back into a life of chronically compromised health, I went back to Dr. Ronda off and on for a growing number of physical ailments. There were times when I couldn't seem to keep food down as I would violently vomit for hours following a meal. This eventually led to lower digestive troubles that included such embarrassing issues as internal hemorrhoids and bleeding that scared me to death. I also developed a mystery pain that was eventually labeled "coccydynia," a fancy name for inflammation of the tailbone.

Now, you might chuckle at that but it was definitely no laughing matter to me. Sitting was often excruciating which made simple tasks like driving a pain in the you-know-what. One time I was set on making it to a family campout in Mammoth Lakes and managed to get through the seven-hour drive with the help of some ibuprofen. However, that backfired on me as the resulting pain from the extended sitting session kept me from being able to sit down much at all for days. I wound up spending much of that vacation lying down in our trailer as the inflammation was through the roof.

I'm fairly certain that Dr. Ronda thought I was on the edge of losing my mind by this point. She would patiently listen to my list of complaints each time we spoke. I'm sure I sounded like a hypochondriac and I definitely felt like one! No matter how many supplements I took or how much healthy food I ate, I wasn't getting any better. Dr. Ronda encouraged me to go get checked out if that would give me the peace of mind I was looking for. So, convinced that I had a tumor hiding in me somewhere, I went to several different medical doctors in an attempt to find the root of my pain.

I grew increasingly discouraged as I couldn't seem to find a physician who would give me more than a few measly minutes before sending me on my way without a diagnosis or real solutions of any kind. X-rays and physical examinations showed no obvious cause for the level of discomfort I was experiencing. I even underwent a colonoscopy in hopes of finding answers, but none came. In my quest for an explanation, Dr. Google was quick to convince me that death was surely at my door. Maybe I really *was* losing my mind.

And then there was my afflicted skin, particularly on my unsightly legs. I was covered in a miserable, itchy rash that kept me awake most nights. My skin was literally falling off. Feeling like a leper, I spent a ridiculous amount of time stuck at home simply because I couldn't bear the pain of wearing pants. I'd slather manuka honey on my legs and whatever other healing concoctions I thought might heal my "severely traumatized" skin, as a doctor called it. I finally buckled and went to a dermatologist for a shot of magic. Thankfully, my cracked, oozing skin did begin healing after that but I was sure I'd be scarred for life.

Sleepless nights became my norm. Sometimes this was due to the mad fits of itching. Other times it was because of the heartburn and vomiting that would ensue whenever I tried to lie down. And when I didn't have a physical ailment stealing my sleep, my restless husband was at the ready.

I've known others throughout my life who have been diagnosed with bipolar disorder, but not one who exhibited symptoms quite like Peter did. A textbook case of bipolar disorder will often look like mood swings, periods of depression followed by periods of heightened mood and increased energy. Everyone exhibits symptoms differently and I don't want to over-simplify my explanation here, but I am not an expert on anything bipolar-related beyond what I experienced personally with my own husband.

Peter was never one who was prone to depression in his life and that didn't change during his four years of battling mental illness. What he did experience was what's called rapid cycling bipolar disorder symptoms characterized by four or more manic or depressive episodes within one year. Seeing as how Peter's manic episodes were at least monthly and often extreme, you might understand the severity of what we were dealing with and how intensely stressful it was.

When manic, Peter would often skip sleep altogether. This meant that I was on night watch, mostly making sure that he didn't leave the house. The ongoing lack of sleep only served to exacerbate my health challenges. I felt trapped in a miserable existence. There was even a point where I was so sick that I spent several days in a nest on my living room floor. I call it a nest because, due to my tailbone pain, I had created a circle of pillows to softly support myself as I cradled a bowl in my lap. The bowl was ready to catch my stomach contents as needed. Let me just say that it wasn't awesome.

Determined to minimize my digestive suffering, I finally opted for hunger over pain. More than once I spent about a week abstaining from food altogether while I allowed my digestive tract to recover from an upset. If I caved in too soon, the smallest morsel would set me off and I'd have to start all over again. And so there I sat, camped out on the living room floor, while my family tiptoed around me as they came and went. Yes, I had arrived alright. I felt like the absolute epitome of pathetic.

JUNE 25, 2012: MY TURNING POINT

Nearly two years to the day since Peter's torment had begun, I found myself at an all-time low. And when you find yourself in a place like that, there are really only two ways to go. One, give up. This will be your life forever until you die, which will probably be soon because Dr. Google said so. Two, get up. Do something about it. Change course. Refuse to go on this way. Fight back!

I remember the day so clearly. Resting under the covers of my bed, honestly feeling unable to function, a surprising wind of motivation blew my way. *I had to get better!* I would not resign myself to this life any longer. It was bad enough that my husband was suffering and unable to be all that he had been to our family before this awful affliction invaded our world. Both of us being taken out was not an option. Our children needed at least one healthy parent.

Inspired by the care I'd received from Dr. Ronda over the years, I decided right then and there that I, too, would become a naturopathic physician. That way, I'd not only be able to heal myself but I'd possibly be able to heal my husband as well! And then we'd go on to support lots of people who were just like us in *their* healings. I could just see it! Already I had purpose in my pain and I was beginning to feel a little bit hopeful.

Without leaving my bed, I began to research various schools and programs that would provide me with the education I needed to achieve my new goal. Like a kid in a candy store, I took in the exciting array of options before me. I couldn't wait to get started. My passion for holistic healing modalities had grown through everything I'd experienced and I wanted nothing more than to pursue this path.

But then came the reality check. I didn't have the time or the financial resources to pursue my new dream. Who was I kidding? It wasn't realistic to think that I could just take off and go to school in my present condition. And who would care for my family while I studied?

Searching the web for possibilities, I stumbled across something that piqued my interest. The Institute for Integrative Nutrition® (IIN®) offered a one-year health coaching certification program. At the time, I'd never even heard of health coaching before. Perusing the website multiple times, I began to wonder if it was a gimmick. I finally gave the institution a phone call to find out more.

I soon learned that if I went through IIN's program, I'd be trained in over one hundred different dietary theories. I'd also be trained in launching my own health coaching practice from the ground up. IIN would even provide me with just about everything I would need to start my own business including my first website and business cards.

I'd be able to start taking on my first clients in only six months as a supervised student health coach. It honestly sounded too good to be true!

IIN turned out to be the real deal and I was chomping at the bit to get started. But first, I needed to talk to my husband. If he wasn't on board, this new plan of mine was not going to happen. So, armed with fresh information, I got out of bed and walked through the house to Peter's office in the garage. I laid it all out for him and tried to answer every question I thought he might ask before he asked it, including the hard numbers. Peter was a successful businessman, after all, so I expected a complete inquisition. But that's not what I got from him.

Sure! Go for it! If anything makes you come alive, it's your passion for wellness. You've been consistent in this direction for many years now and I don't see that changing. That's the kind of investment I feel confident in making.

Peter went on to pledge his support for me and my new career path not only with the necessary finances, but also with his time and energy. He wanted to help me make a business plan. He wanted to help care for the children more to free me up. He was completely in this with me. I was utterly overwhelmed with both disbelief and gratitude. Thankfully we were able to make this decision together during a time when his mind was stable and his thinking clear. Even though he wasn't able to follow through on all of his initial promises, I knew that in his heart of hearts he loved and supported me. That's who the real Peter was. Now can you see why I couldn't give up on this man?

A WHOLE NEW ME

I wasted no time. From the moment I registered with IIN, I had immediate access to a library of fascinating lectures through an app on my phone. I couldn't get enough of it. The program hadn't even officially begun yet, but until then I was fed a steady diet of information provided by some of the world's top wellness professionals. They clearly knew their stuff and I was soaking it all up like a sponge.

With my earbuds in place, I got out of bed and began to do things I hadn't done in quite a long time. As I made my way through the IIN library of lectures in my phone, I cleaned my house. I took long walks. I listened intently as I ran errands in the car. I didn't think much about these mundane tasks as my mind was preoccupied by all the satisfying information I was absorbing. This went on for days and weeks until something miraculous happened. I became well again.

It didn't happen overnight, but it did happen rather quickly. One by one, my physical afflictions began dropping off. I didn't have room for that baggage in my new life, so subconsciously I sent it packing. Over the course of a few short months, my physical troubles were crowded out by new dreams and fresh hope. A whole new me was born. And, best of all, I was really and truly happy, filled with a joy that wasn't dependent upon my circumstances.

It was this newfound joy and strength that served to carry me through yet another unfortunate season of grief. After four years of journeying with Peter through the injustices and calamity that mental illness so often brings, our lives were forever changed once again on June 2, 2014. Peter had taken off the night before in a state of manic confusion and I hadn't heard from him since. With a sickening feeling in my gut that he wouldn't be coming back this time, I did my best to alert family as to what I sensed was an urgent need for intervention on Peter's behalf.

At about eleven o'clock the next morning, I had just returned home from taking five-year-old Alyma to a doctor's appointment when I was greeted by two female law enforcement officers. I went outside to speak to them in my driveway knowing that they came with news concerning Peter. After making sure that everyone else in our family was safe and accounted for, they informed me that my husband had been found deceased early that morning in Ventura County. As a result of his mania, he had attempted a feat too great for his human abilities, a feat that would cost him his life here on earth.

Although the blow of this heartbreaking news was obviously devastating, I was at peace. Not only was Peter finally free from torment, but he was already enjoying eternity with his Creator. I had many questions racing through my mind, to be sure. But most of all I felt an assurance deep within me that the kids and I would come through this tragedy with our hard-earned resilience and faith in God's ability to redeem any situation. And that's exactly what happened.

Breaking Free from a Toxic Life

• • •

When I was young, I enjoyed life from within a safety bubble that protected me from any kind of major suffering. Coming from a family of faith, I believed and trusted in God. In my mind, dedicating my life to God secured me a degree of what I will call "trial insurance." I was fairly certain that, somewhere in the Bible, I had been promised special protection as a Christian.

God wouldn't give me more than I could handle. God would keep my loved ones and me safe at all times. God had a wonderful plan for my life, which had to mean that it was impossible for my steady stream of fears to ever be realized. I believed it all to be completely true.

Should we just stop here and laugh for a minute? Clearly anyone with a bit of life experience can see how ludicrous my trial insurance theory was. And anyone who has really read the Bible knows that the apostles themselves endured greater trials than I could ever imagine. In fact, they likely would have enjoyed much easier lives had they not answered the call to live out their earthly days for Jesus.

I'm not blaming my church, my parents or anyone else for putting such ideas in my young head. This was a belief that I had contrived based on a combination of my own immature interpretations of the Bible and the fact that, growing up, life was pretty easy. My experience in a middle class family where we never seemed to suffer much supported my notion that we had earned special protection rights. I reasoned that we must be living in the center of God's will for our lives, that magical place where my imaginary safety bubble could be found.

Well, life is full of surprises and mine has been no exception. As it turns out, none of us are promised a trial-free life at all. On the contrary, we seem to be born into this world with guaranteed suffering ahead. None of us are exempt from loss or heartache. We all lose loved ones along the paths of our lives. We each have our turn with being heartbroken in some way, possibly even multiple times. By now, I am clear on this. Adulthood has made sure to instruct me in all that my childhood somehow spared me from.

STRESS IS HERE TO STAY

As grown adults, I think we can all agree that none of us maintain special protection from the myriad of stressors that appear throughout our lives. We have career and financial pressures. We suffer from mental, emotional and physical strain on a regular basis. Our relationships can oftentimes be one of our greatest sources of anxiety.

And then there are those particularly stressful times when an unexpected traumatic event such as an illness, an injury or possibly a death could strike. Have I left anyone out?

As Americans, we are downright stressed out. Just look at us. We can hardly remember how to eat and sit down at the same time anymore. Many of us run ourselves into the ground just trying to keep up with these overly full lives we have created. It's a legitimate challenge to avoid falling into the rat race that life threatens to become!

While we should certainly do our part to lower our individual anxiety levels, the fact of the matter is that stress is here to stay. Whether as an infrequent visitor or an unwelcome constant companion, we will all continue to navigate stress in some way. We're in this thing together. While some may seem to have it easier than others, none of us are exempt from life's challenges. We may be able to learn how to lessen or altogether avoid certain types of stress, but much of it is unfortunately inescapable.

We don't have to wait to be in crisis mode before we begin to learn some healthy stress management tools. In fact, it's best to practice these tools *before* entering a crisis. That way, when the heat is on we will already have some healthy coping habits in place. It will serve us all well, then, if we can learn and practice the tools I'm about to share with you.

Perhaps you're like I was a few years ago, currently finding yourself smack dab in the middle of your own personal nightmare, unsure of how to wake up and move on with life. When everything seems to be out of order or in some stage of neglect, it can be hard to know where to begin to turn it all around.

Well, take heart because it's not too late for you. Just stick with me through the pages of this book and I'll do my best to make this an easy-to-use guide for you. I'll share stories of my own battles and the hard lessons I've learned along the way. I believe that you'll find yourself somewhere in these pages and instinctively know what it is you need to focus on.

Just remember that this is a process. The fact that you're even reading this book tells me that you're on the right track. It's not necessary, or even recommended, that you attempt the implementation of every single tool within these pages at once. Don't rush it. Try out a new tool each day and see what feels like a good fit for you. Keep it simple.

PRIMARY FOOD: BEYOND WHAT'S ON YOUR PLATE

Before we progress, I want to introduce a concept to you that will lay the groundwork for all that follows. When I attended the Institute for Integrative Nutrition, I had many "aha!" moments. Learning about the concept of Primary and Secondary Foods was one of those moments for me. It was within this philosophy that my own experience finally made complete sense. For me, this answered the questions I had as to why I could eat so well and take such good care of myself yet still suffer from chronic illness.

Have you ever known anyone like that? I know I have. Years ago, I was acquainted with a middle-aged woman I'll call Sandy. Sandy should have been a picture of health based on her diet and the quantity of supplements she was taking. She seemed to be knowledgeable about nutrition and yet, no matter what she tried, her long list of ailments simply would not relent. One of her family members confided in me that Sandy was just a hypochondriac. But how could this be possible? I didn't understand it.

And then there was a relative of mine I'll call Mary who was the very first health nut I ever knew. She was "crunchy" before crunchy was cool. (The term "crunchy" here refers to an all-natural hippie-esque lifestyle that tends to involve eating lots of granola—thus the crunch.)

Juicing was first introduced to me as a child through Mary. At her house, we were sure to be fed carob over chocolate and raw honey over white sugar. Her countertops were perpetually littered with more supplements than I knew what to do with. Even still, she was sickly all of the years that I knew her. This never made sense to me until I learned about the concept of Primary and Secondary Food.

The Institute for Integrative Nutrition® (IIN®) founder, Joshua Rosenthal, coined the terms Primary Food and Secondary Food. Primary Food refers to everything that feeds us that is not edible food. Primary Food (such as our careers, relationships, spirituality, physical activity, finances, education, environment, social life, and other lifestyle factors) plays an equal if, not more significant, role in the quality of our lives than what is on our plates.

In contrast, Secondary Food is the actual food we eat: fruits, vegetables, grains, proteins, and fats. Secondary Food does not provide the fulfilment that Primary Food provides, but oftentimes we use it to suppress our hunger for Primary Food.

Remember, people need more than their nutritional needs met in order to be healthy; they need love, movement, stability, adventure, purpose, and creativity in order to thrive.

Just think of all that feeds us outside of what we put in our mouths. It is these aspects of our lives that bring us energy, joy, vitality, and basically make our lives worth living. In the absence of healthy Primary Food, we essentially die a slow death due to either toxic overload or starvation. You'll know you're deficient in nourishing Primary Food when your eating habits begin spiraling out of control. Emotional eating is simply your subconscious self trying to meet a non-physical need with food.

THE INTEGRATIVE NUTRITION® PLATE

The Institute for Integrative Nutrition® (IIN®) teaches a number of dietary theories and concepts. The Integrative Nutrition® Plate, pictured below, conveys nutritional and lifestyle guidelines for optimal health and wellbeing. Unlike most government diagrams, which focus primarily on food, the Integrative Nutrition® Plate incorporates relationships, spirituality, career, and physical activity as four additional areas we must nourish in order to thrive.

© 2013 Integrative Nutrition, Inc. | Reprinted with permission.
No further copying and/or republication is authorized.
Integrative Nutrition Inc. does not endorse the content contained in this book

PRIMARY FOOD IN REAL LIFE

Back in 2011 and early 2012, I was a classic picture of a person suffering from a Primary Food deficiency. My husband was trapped in a false reality. My marriage to a now barely recognizable man was held together by a thread. While my faith was intact, I was disappointed with God. Feeling forgotten by Him and many others, I wondered if I hadn't been outright abandoned and tossed aside.

For the most part, I had no life outside of my chaotic home. No passions, no hobbies, nothing that really made me feel happy to be alive aside from three young blessings who were depending on me, their mother, to be there for them. I was sick and I was miserable no matter how dialed in my diet was.

If you remember my story from chapter two, you'll recall that I quickly bounced back from my physical ailments after enrolling in the IIN health coaching program. Why do you think that was? Can you see the shift that had occurred in my Primary Food? My actual diet didn't change at all, however by choosing to make one adjustment after another in my Primary Food, I became well again.

Let's go back to my friend Sandy. If I were to tell you that she had been enduring an emotionally abusive marriage for many years, would you possibly gain a clue into her frustrating health issues? Although I credit her loyalty in remaining with her husband of at least a few decades, it later became clear to me that this relationship was poisoning her. This is a typical example of a long-term toxic relationship and, as you now know, relationships are a vital component of our Primary Food.

As for the crunchy relative of mine, Mary, she had become a product of a number of Primary Food deficiencies over the course of her life. She maintained a strong spiritual practice all of her days, but just about every other area of her life was either toxic or deficient in some way.

Her marriage was riddled with conflict, something that she seemed to endure out of a sense of duty. While she was encouraged countless times to at least take a short walk down the street, she refused to participate in any physical activities. The majority of her time was spent between her bed and various reclining chairs at home. As a result, her social life was very limited. Her mental, physical and emotional state weakened with age until her body sadly gave out. I think we can probably agree that this isn't an example of the thriving kind of life we all aspire to enjoy. Healthy eating alone just isn't going to cut it.

If you were my health coaching client, I could talk to you all day long about how to eat better. But I would be doing you a disservice if I ignored your Primary Food. As a matter of fact, I once had a client who struggled with a number of health issues centering around numerous digestive and skin-related troubles. She and I worked together for six months and saw little to no progress.

Through the process of uncovering growth areas in her Primary Food, it became clear that she hated her job. Ruled by her employer, she had very little time to live her life outside of work. Shopping for and cooking healthy meals wasn't often possible because of her long work hours. Exercise fell by the wayside. Her stress levels were sky high. And while she'd considered stepping away from it all and starting her own business, she wasn't sure that she was ready.

However, towards the end of our six months together, she did take the leap and quit her job. Suddenly she had time to sleep, time to go for walks and workouts at the gym. She quickly adapted to a new, more relaxed pace of life in which *she* was now in the driver's seat. At last she could truly enjoy her life again.

It wasn't until a few months after our six-month program together had ended that I received a celebratory note from this former client of mine. She wanted to let me know that she had, indeed, finally overcome the physical challenges she had suffered from. Even though I was no longer working with her, she had continued to practice the tools I coached her in. Now she was eating well, exercising, enjoying a fulfilling relationship and finding success and fulfillment in running her own business. That's what I call thriving!

Aside from all of this, my former client attributed her breakthrough to the fact that I'd encouraged her to make a change in her career life. While the prospect of her quitting her job made us both a little nervous as she gave up a degree of security for a while, in the long run she gained so much more. The unfortunate symptoms of a toxic work situation fell away as she embraced her new path of freedom.

Sure, I can teach you how to clean up your diet and eat right. And I will talk a little about how to do that in this book. Secondary Food *is* an important piece of the puzzle. But, in light of my own personal experience, I believe that I can best support you by providing the knowledge and tools required to access the good health that becomes available to us when we break free from a toxic lifestyle. It's time to trade in our unhealthy Primary Food and we're going to do that together one step at a time. Are you ready?

Section
TWO

· · ·

**THE 30-DAY
GUIDE**

ABOUT THE 30-DAY GUIDE

...

By now you understand why the tools and concepts I'm focusing on in the pages that follow center around choosing healthy Primary Food over toxic alternatives. As you progress through the pages of this book, each day you'll learn at least one way to make a simple mindset shift or lifestyle adjustment that will gradually direct you towards the happy, fulfilling life you've been longing for.

Remember, it *is* possible to thrive in your current situation. Please don't allow yourself to become discouraged by looking too far ahead. Together we're going to take this journey one day at a time. A month from now, you'll look back and see that the subtle shifts you've made have worked together to set you on a new course. And this is just the beginning of a thriving life spent practicing your new strategies.

Just think of this book as your toolbox. Keep it with you for now. When you need a tool to help you get through a rough moment, flip it open. It doesn't matter which tool you pick, just pick one and give it a try. If it's what you need at the time, then great! If not, try another until you find one, two, or maybe three tools that take you in the right direction. With consistent practice, you'll soon see glimpses of your very own personal transformation in progress.

This book can act as your guide through a thirty-day holistic makeover or you can spread it out over several weeks. Perhaps you have two or three days a week during which you can set aside fifteen minutes to read a short chapter and practice one new tool for that day. The important thing is that you *do* make the time and put what you read into practice. I'm excited to see where this journey takes you, so let's get started!

CHOOSING HAPPY

• • •

"I am more and more convinced that our happiness or our unhappiness depends far more on the way we meet the events of life than on the nature of those events themselves."

KARL WILHELM VON HUMBOLDT

• • •

We've all heard the saying, "You are what you eat." No one can really argue with this, right? Life-giving foods produce life in our bodies. Junk foods deliver exactly that—junk. It's not rocket science. As we choose which foods (or food-like substances) to put in our mouths, we're essentially choosing the building blocks of our health with every bite. We'll talk more about this later on.

For today, I want to apply this same principle to our thoughts. We really *are* what we *think*. Just as we each made a deliberate decision in regards to what we ate for breakfast this morning, we will each choose the thoughts we think and the emotions we feel throughout the day. Everything that we do or say begins with a thought.

The mind is a battlefield where the war between healthy and toxic thinking wages on every waking moment of the day. And as we already know, that powerless feeling we often struggle with while walking through trying times is lying to us, trying to convince us that we don't have the power to choose how we feel. But we are *not* powerless. While our particular circumstances may remain outside of our control, we still have the opportunity to be powerful today.

I have good news for you. That unfair situation you may be in right now doesn't make your decisions—YOU do. I realize that it's easy to feel justified in choosing angry, resentful, unforgiving thoughts, but this type of thinking isn't going to do us any favors. Yes, stuff happens in life that just plain stinks. But we can still "choose happy" at any given moment.

The intentional selection of the thoughts we think shapes who we are on a cellular level. The way we respond in our relationships, at our jobs and in all the various aspects of our personal lives stems from what's going on upstairs. The chemicals released in our brains travel throughout our bodies, expressing themselves according to their true nature. This is how we literally become the thoughts that we think.

If you recall the story of my turning point in chapter two, the choice to step outside of my own misery and into something that made me happy resulted in the complete turnaround of my physical health. How did this happen? Well, when we think, we feel. Prior to my decision to make a change, my thoughts and feelings were far from happy.

My physical body followed suit. My liver was grumpy, my digestive system was irritable and my skin was just plain distressed!

When I later made the choice to think and feel happier thoughts, my body again responded in kind. All of that imbalance and upset going on inside of me as a result of prolonged stress couldn't last amidst the flood of happy hormones that took over. The chemicals in our brains have that much power.

For many of us, thinking ourselves happy does not come easily. Years and years of negative training can develop strong habits in our thought lives that may take time to wire out.

Perhaps we lean automatically towards pessimism or criticism due to the environment we were raised in. Or maybe we tend to focus on what appears to be an unfair set of cards we've been dealt in life. We come to expect bad things to happen. We anticipate negative results and, because that's what we're focusing on, that's what we get. This is a toxic thought pattern, a bad habit.

In the fascinating book *The Power of Habit,* author Charles Duhigg demonstrates how habits are created and established in the brain. Thoughts are essentially habits, beginning from seeds and, if allowed to take root and grow, develop into full-grown trees with a complete set of branches. This is actually good news where positive thoughts and habits are concerned. Through the act of choosing happy thoughts, we can grow happy trees!

Our kids never seem to tire of watching Netflix episodes of Bob Ross painting his "happy little trees" on canvas. I have to admit, watching his oil painted scenes unfold with each stroke of the brush *is* mesmerizing, especially for someone like me who lacks such artistic talent. Most of our children demonstrate impressive artistic giftings. Even our youngest children have already surpassed my painting and drawing abilities.

What I *can* paint, though, are happy little trees on the canvas of my own psyche. No one else can paint them for me. With each stroke of my mental paintbrush, I possess the creative ability to color and transform the landscape of my mind. And so do you.

The bottom line is this; our emotional body is our governor. How we think is how we feel. How we feel dictates our reality as expressed through our physical health. So, if we're bent on entertaining negative thoughts, we're going to feel a whole gamut of negative emotions such as confusion, anger, irritation, worry, bitterness and so on. The chemicals associated with these feelings are released by the brain and sent off to circulate throughout our bodies, resulting in physical health that parallels our thoughts and feelings.

And that was me! Or at least it was until I traded in my negative thought habits for positive ones. Feelings of hope and happiness grew until, one by one, my physical ailments dropped away. Fear and hopelessness couldn't hang around any longer once love and joy arrived to replace them.

Now that we're armed with this life-transforming information and a little of the science behind it, the key to success lies in self-awareness. When we wake up in the morning, what are our first thoughts? When we engage with others, are we focusing more on what they're thinking about us or on what *we* think about ourselves? Does what we imagine others are thinking about us determine how we feel?

These are just a few examples of questions we should be asking ourselves throughout the day. Breaking old thought patterns requires this kind of deliberate self-assessment, often times affording us the opportunity to stop toxic thinking in its tracks. The mind-body connection is very real and cannot be ignored. Science clearly shows us that healthy thoughts create healthy bodies. We can think ourselves healthier, happier, and more peaceful despite what's going on around us.

LET'S TAKE A VACATION

Do you know that our brains cannot distinguish the difference between perceived stress and actual stress? For example, closing your eyes and imagining yourself being attacked by an intruder in your home produces the same exact stress hormones as if you were actually being attacked.

On the flip side, closing our eyes and placing ourselves in the dreamy vacation spot of our choice, perhaps lying on a white sand beach with a piña colada in hand, produces real relaxation chemicals in the brain just as if we were actually there.

Now, I know we'd both rather experience the real deal, but science can testify to the fact that imagined vacations can be equally as beneficial as actual ones. So what have we got to lose? Let's take a vacation together right now! I'm going to show you how to do this and then you can close your eyes and go on vacation for as long as you'd like.

Let's start by finding a quiet place and getting comfortable. As for me, I have six kids at home. Finding quiet sometimes requires a brief escape to the shower or perhaps the car in my driveway. If you're a parent, I'm sure you know what I mean. Do what you need to do.

Now think of a relaxing place you've been in the past or one you'd like to be at in the future. Visualize your surroundings. What do you see? Engage your senses. Imagine the soothing sounds, the feel of the sun on your skin perhaps. What does it smell like?

Because my mental vacation is taking place back "home" on the Big Island, I have my favorite beach in my mind. The sand beneath me feels warm. I can hear the tropical birds and the sound of the waves rolling in and out as the salty air clings to my skin.

Now focus on your breath. As you inhale for four breaths and exhale for about six, imagine yourself breathing in peace and breathing out stress. Breathe in everything that is relaxing to you about this vacation spot. Breathe out all that you wish to rid yourself of. Continue this for five minutes or for as long as you have the time to enjoy it.

Taking a mental vacation is just one tool that can help us "choose happy" each day. I know that it might feel like a small step now, but in the days ahead we'll be adding to this toolbox. With each conscious choice, with each new tool, you will be creating new healthy habits in your brain.

• • •

By the end of thirty days,

I believe you'll be surprised

when you look back and

see how much lighter

and happier you feel.

• • •

GETTING ANCHORED

• • •

"In order to realize the worth of the anchor,
we need to feel the stress of the storm."

CORRIE TEN BOOM

• • •

Growing up in a place where visits to the lake helped us endure the summer heat, I've enjoyed a fair amount of time boating. As a child, my grandfather took us out on his boat every summer. He seemed to find great pleasure in whipping my siblings and I across the turbulent surface of the water on a tube until either we simply couldn't hold on any longer or the tube flipped over, tossing our bodies in all directions. And then we'd beg for more!

My husband and I have our own boat with which we amuse ourselves by towing our wildly screaming children around that same lake. Between tubing sessions, we like to find a sheltered cove near the shore, throw our anchor overboard and cool ourselves off in the refreshing blue water. There's been a time or two when, in our eagerness to dive in, we've forgotten to first release the anchor. An unmanned, unanchored vessel is at the mercy of the waves in a situation like this. It doesn't take much to send a boat off in the wrong direction, oftentimes straight into a rocky shore.

During times of more unsettled waters, our boat has drifted off a bit despite having set the anchor. This happens because it's not the weight of the anchor alone that keeps a boat firmly in place. If you drop an anchor into a mushy lake bottom, there's nothing for the arms of the anchor to grab hold of. Instead, an anchor must be embedded into rocks to avoid the slipping that can otherwise occur.

What is true for watercraft is also true for our personal lives. In the absence of a secure anchor, we are at the mercy of the waves. The bigger the waves, the more powerful the storm, the more we might find ourselves being tossed about should we be caught off-guard and unanchored. And nothing puts an anchor to the test like a bonafide storm.

Getting anchored might not be the most simple tool in the toolbox. But I have intentionally placed this tool early in our journey towards thriving together for good reason. There is no way I could have made it through the violent storms I've faced in my life had I not been firmly anchored. What anchors you might not be the same thing that anchors me. And that's okay. The important point here is that we have an anchor that can be trusted. This is exactly what I want to focus on today.

Common sense would tell us that it's probably not the best idea to wait until we're smack dab in the middle of some precarious waters to discover whether we have an anchor on board or not. One considerable wave is all it takes to throw a boat, or perhaps a life, off course. But sometimes it happens and, in that instance, we do what must be done. Cast the anchor, find as much security as possible in the midst of the storm and hold on for dear life.

The first step is to *have* an anchor. For me, that is my faith and the steadfast hope I glean from that. Throughout my life, my faith has kept me stable while the circumstances surrounding me challenged my direction. I haven't veered too far off course because of my faith, my unseen anchor. This is largely due to my being raised with a foundation of faith. Realizing that not everyone goes through his or her early years with such security in place, I'm very grateful for this.

For me, hope without faith is merely a desire for something good to happen in the future. It's wishful thinking. But when I add my faith to the equation, I find a hope that is more than just crossing my fingers and yearning for the best. This type of hope doesn't waver because it's rooted in the unchanging faithfulness of God. Confident hope is faith applied to your future.

Maintaining hope means keeping our well of hope full. Being a visual person, I like to imagine an actual well that I can draw from when I need it. Whether we realize it or not, we continually make deposits and withdrawals from our wells of hope each and every day through our thoughts and our choices. When you feel yourself being overtaken by despair, that's a good sign that your hope well is running dry. I'd be willing to bet that fear, the enemy of hope, has made too many withdrawals and left you drowning in discouragement.

Believe me, I know how paralyzing hopelessness can be. Hopelessness commands that we give up and stop trying because it doesn't matter what we do, we're still going to be stuck in the same dreadful situation. Hopelessness tells us to look at our broken past and wonder why we should even bother believing for anything better to come in the future. It's during these times that we must make a deliberate choice to tune out fear and cling to hope.

I'm not here to tell you what your anchor should be, but I will say this. If you believe that your anchor lies in a person, then prepare yourself for troubled waters. Wrapping the arms of our anchor around another human being is just about as effective as planting our boat's anchor into the soft lake bottom with nothing to really grab hold of. Even on my best days, I know that I'm not likely to pass as a suitable anchor for anyone. Yes, we can provide strength to one another but we will make mistakes and let people down. It is *vital* to have an anchor that is greater and more reliable than our fallible human abilities.

It's a good idea to take an honest look at what our lives are anchored to from time to time. If you already have your anchor secured, then great. You'll find that the days ahead will only serve to strengthen that anchor. But if you feel that you need support in discovering a rock strong enough to anchor your life to, I'm here to encourage you in that direction.

Take some time today to reach out to someone you trust, someone who you feel has modeled the type of strength you long for. Ask for guidance and it will come. Today is your day to take a step towards securing an anchor in your own life.

• • •

Immoveable, confident hope is

available to each of us and

is absolutely able to hold us

firmly through even the most

powerful storms in our lives.

• • •

MASTERING FEAR

• • •

"Courage is resistance to fear, mastery
of fear, not absence of fear."

MARK TWAIN

• • •

Even with my solid foundation in life, the storm that I walked through from 2010–2014 required an anchor upgrade. Of course I had no way of knowing this at the time, but looking back I can see how God, in His sovereign goodness, provided exactly what I needed before the storm touched down.

Shortly after our arrival on the Big Island in January of 2009, a sweet woman by the name of Debbie invited me to a women's Bible study in her home. Even in the small island town of Hawi (pronounced *ha-VEE*), Debbie is a mover and a shaker. Not only is she an incredible wife and mother on the home front, she's also active in her community on multiple levels. She's the kind of woman I'd like to be when I grow up.

I wasn't in Kohala for long before I recognized the "mother hen" mantle that Debbie seemed to wear effortlessly. The young mothers in the area, many of us displaced from our own mothers back on the mainland, were drawn to her like flies on, well, just about everything in Hawaii. And if you've lived in Hawaii, particularly in the rural areas as we did, you know what I mean.

It didn't matter that most of us young mothers had at least a few highly active children running wildly about. Debbie welcomed them, loved on them and even spent time doing crafts and playing games with them. Basically, she was every young mother's dream in a surrogate grandmother.

Sharing similar passions, Debbie and I made an easy connection. While I had only briefly met one or two of the young ladies who attended Debbie's Bible study, I couldn't turn down the invitation for a weekly opportunity to be in her home. As the new haole in town, I wasn't going to make new friends in this foreign place unless I stepped outside of my comfort zone. (The term "haole," pronounced *HOW-lee*, refers mainly to white people.)

If you've done many Bible studies in your lifetime, you've probably heard of the best-selling author and dynamic teacher, Beth Moore. She had released her study on the biblical character of Esther not long before our move to Hawaii. And this was the study that Debbie's women's group was participating in. It was a study on courage, on pushing past our feelings of inadequacy and victoriously walking through overwhelming situations.

Heck, I had just left everything that was familiar to me behind on the mainland and moved my pregnant self, along with my family, to a remote speck on the map in the middle of the Pacific Ocean. I figured I was doing pretty well in the courage department by this point. We were in paradise now, over the hump of a daunting transoceanic moving process. Life could only get better from here.

Diving into the Beth Moore study was more intense than I had anticipated. There was homework required five days a week. We had a workbook to keep up with and reading to complete. And then we got to a point early in the study where we were asked to write down our worst fears. I found myself feeling paralyzed.

Acknowledging my fears, particularly my deepest, darkest fears, was never something I had allowed myself to do. It was bad enough to *think* of my fears, and even worse to *write them down*. Penciling my fears out on paper was akin to bringing them into the light for everyone to see, causing me to feel exposed and vulnerable to attack.

Although my childhood had been mostly secure, I still battled fear more than the average child. My fears were irrational, possibly stemming from recurring nightmares and small glimpses into movies like *The Wizard of Oz* and *E.T.* I had zero tolerance for exposure to anything that might add to my vivid imagination once the lights were turned out at night. The unseen evil beings that lurked under my bed or in my closet, the demons that were sure to chase me while I ran down the hallway of our home in the dark, they were still out there.

As an adult, I had mostly learned to keep my anxiety at bay. But I was sure that either speaking or writing my secret fears down would burst my bubble of protection, somehow giving permission for them to come to pass. I couldn't allow that to happen.

I wrestled with this assignment. I prayed. I challenged my own beliefs about the perceived power of acknowledging my fears. Could completing this assignment actually bring my fears to pass? Well, I would find out.

In my mind's eye, I can still see the lines in the workbook upon which I penciled out my top three worst fears. As is true for most mothers, at the top of the list was something awful happening to one of my children. Losing one of them would surely wreck me forever.

Also high on my list was losing my husband and the father of our children. The very idea was unbearable. I nervously wrote it down and moved on, afraid to entertain these thoughts more than necessary.

What was the point behind this peculiar assignment, anyway? Well, if you're familiar with the Old Testament story of Esther, you know that she was beautiful and brave. A common Jewish orphan raised by her uncle, Esther (then Hadassah) was recruited during an empire-wide search into the palace of the Persian king, Ahasuerus. After a year of intentional preparation, Esther was at last presented to the king and would eventually become the queen of Persia. Meanwhile, her Jewish identity remained hidden.

In time, the fate of the Jewish people living in Persia was doomed. The queen was confronted by her worst fears; either she had to risk her own life by approaching the king uninvited, revealing her Jewish identity, or her beloved uncle Mordecai, and all of the Jews in Persia along with him, would perish at the hand of an evil man who had gained the king's favor.

After much prayer and fasting, Esther was resolute. She faced her fears and made her decision, famously declaring, "I will go in to the king and plead my people's case, even though it means breaking the law. And if I die, then I die!" (Esther 4:16b, The Voice)

The story of Esther reads like a suspense novel, full of evil plotting, romance and—finally—redemption. While there is much that can be drawn from this ancient story, what inspired me at the time of my study was the way Esther made peace with her fears. She surrendered the outcome of her own life and the lives of her people to her faith and trust in God. Even if it meant death, she would trust.

Over the course of this nine-week study, I would also be stretched to face and master my worst fears. I wrote in my workbook by the end of the nine weeks:

Even if I lose my children, God has a good plan for my life.

Even if I lose my husband, I trust in God's ability to bring redemption to my family.

Even if I lose my own life, God still has a good plan for my husband and my children.

I replaced my fears with my faith. I wrestled through it, wrote it down and I spoke it five days a week during this Beth Moore study. Each time I did so, the grip of fear on my life was weakened to the point of near powerlessness as my confidence in God's ability to redeem any situation grew.

Even if my worst fears become a reality, I will be okay.

At the end of nine weeks, I believed it. When my fears presented themselves, I could face them and smile. My faith had been upgraded. I now possessed an anchor strong enough to carry me through the raging storm that was heading my way.

We are each on an individual journey, each at different stages and facing a wide array of unique challenges. The obstacles I faced might be similar to yours or they might be drastically different. What we have in common is that we are human beings in need of a power greater than ourselves in order to overcome fear. Perhaps you are in touch with that power already. If this isn't the case, reach out to me or someone else you trust for guidance.

This is my own story and I share it openly with you. Take from it what you will. I cannot tell you what might be standing in the way of you having a faith that is strong enough to dismantle your fears. I can only tell you that it really is possible to remain hopeful, even joyful, in the midst of violent seas. But to do so, we must master our fears.

When you feel ready, take some time to practice the fear-busting exercise I described above. Identify your worst fears and replace them with faith. Today's your day to deconstruct the fears that may be lying to you and holding you hostage.

· · ·

Whatever you're going through

today, please know that there's still

a good plan for your life. Not even

the realization of your worst fears

can take that away from you.

· · ·

MAINTAINING FOCUS

• • •

*"It is during our darkest moments that
we must focus to see the light."*

ARISTOTLE

• • •

As far back as I can remember, I have loved a good storm. Somehow powerful storms serve to remind me of my place in the world. I am as entirely incapable of controlling the weather as I am the tribulations that blow through my life. It seems that all I can control is my focus in the midst of a raging storm, and my focus determines my response.

It was at a winter camp at the age of thirteen that I first recall learning the importance of maintaining focus during a storm. As a youth group, we had traveled together by bus to Bend, Oregon. We looked forward to playing in the snow and the opportunity to ski the slopes of Mt. Bachelor, for those who were so inclined. There would be time to worship and lean in to God surrounded by dear friends, old and new alike.

During one such evening, I sat only partially listening to our camp speaker, Eddie Rentz. While I do remember the speaker's name, I can't recall the songs we sang. I don't remember the message Eddie spoke to our group. I *can* tell you the name of the cute boy who had my mind more than a little distracted. Other than that, I really only remember the moment when Eddie turned his attention toward me, confidently pointed me out in the crowd and asked me to stand up.

Who was I to be called out by this man, a total stranger? Suddenly I was keenly aware of the fact that I hadn't been paying much attention to his message and silently hoped that I wouldn't be asked any questions. I would certainly look like a fool to everyone around me!

But Eddie didn't have any questions for me at all, thank God. Instead he had a message. Still pointing at me as I nervously stood up among my peers, Eddie declared:

> *Young lady, you will face challenging storms in your life. But don't be afraid. The Lord would say to you, remember Peter. And here's why. Peter found himself on a boat in the midst of a massive storm. Jesus, walking on water, appeared to Peter and called him to step out of the boat onto the water. This seemed impossible! Yet when Peter kept his eyes focused on Jesus, he was able to walk on water even while the storm raged on around him. It was only when he shifted his focus from Jesus to the storm and the waves that fear entered and Peter began to sink, crying out to the Lord to save him.*

As I absorbed the words spoken by our camp speaker, I felt the heaviness of it. I felt the ominous-yet-hopeful message. Most of all, I felt the call and the challenge to be single-focused rather than swayed and distracted by all that was going on around me. I remained standing in this solemn moment, not wanting to miss any of it.

Eddie began to pray for me. As he did, I sensed a tall, warm presence behind me. "Oh, it must be Kari," I thought to myself. Kari was my friend and she was tall, at least compared to my five-foot-four self. I felt reassured by the strength of the large, comforting hand resting upon my left shoulder. The air felt electric around me as my body seemed to spark from head to toe. No longer concerned with the room full of eyes facing my way, I remained standing with my own eyes sealed shut, hands open in a receiving position in front of me.

When Eddie's prayer was complete, I felt compelled to turn around to the friend standing behind me. Reaching out for a hug, I opened my eyes. My heart suddenly jumped and I quietly gasped upon discovering that no one was visible after all. I questioned those around me, asking who had been there. But all reports confirmed that no one had been seen next to me.

This was not my first experience with an unseen holy presence. I was not alarmed at all. Instead, I felt seen by the One who was unseen. This message, this supernatural touch, marked me and has remained one of the most spiritually significant moments of my life.

The story of Peter walking on the water has continued to resurface when I need a reminder to maintain my focus. And even though I've heard the story countless times, there seems to be no end to the revelation that can be drawn from it. Just a few weeks ago, I was sitting in a morning service at The Stirring listening to Pastor Nathan Edwardson share his own spin on this familiar narrative. He made a point that I'd never considered before. He said, "Peter never would have walked on water if there hadn't been a storm."

My heart leapt when I heard this as my spirit internally shouted, "YES!" in complete agreement. It's so true! No, I never would have volunteered to go through the wild storms that I have. But it is because of my determination to maintain focus during those storms that I have not only survived, but I have experienced exhilarating moments far outside of my comfort zone. I'm certain that I wouldn't be who I am today if not for those opportunities to be challenged in the midst of a violent storm.

I have to believe that this is perhaps one of the main reasons why Jesus didn't calm the storm and provide a perfectly serene environment for Peter to step out into. No, instead he allowed the storm to rage on while speaking peace to the person in the storm. He wouldn't consider robbing Peter of his big moment, his opportunity to master his fear, walk on water and have the exciting story told and retold for centuries to come.

Trust me, I know how easy it is to be overwhelmed and altogether consumed by the vastness of a storm. But no matter how scary the storm may feel, it will pass. When it does, you'll be found standing stronger than ever before if you can remember to shut out all that threatens to distract you from maintaining a single focus.

No matter the storm that you may be facing today or will face in the future, the way through it is essentially the same. Maintain focus not on the waves, not on the wind or the deafening claps of thunder, but on hope's guiding light.

...

Is your focus on the storm

or on hope today? Focusing on

hope gives you the ability to

embrace peace no matter how

fierce the storm may seem.

...

PRESSING PAUSE

• • •

"Practice the pause. When in doubt, pause.
When angry, pause. When tired, pause.
When stressed, pause. And when you pause, pray."

AUTHOR UNKNOWN

• • •

After spending several weeks getting re-stabilized back on the main-land, our family had returned to Kohala at the end of October 2010 eager to get back to what we hoped would be a normal life. Peter hadn't shown any real signs of this supposed bipolar disorder while in California, so we assumed the best; the worst was over.

Once we returned to the island, however, things didn't go as we had hoped. It was only a matter of a few days before I began to see the signs of mania returning in Peter. Bracing myself, I begrudgingly stepped into the next episode of my own personal horror film. At least now I'd been through this a couple of times and knew a little of what to expect. Someone suffering from a manic episode can be completely unpredictable, however, so I was on constant high alert.

Since Peter's symptoms had only surfaced in Hawaii and he seemed to be fine while in California, I found Hawaii to be the common denominator. Maybe there was just something about this place that didn't agree with him, something unseen perhaps. After many calls to friends and family back on the mainland, I made the difficult decision to move our family back to California for a time.

Peter, however, was not easily convinced. With wide-eyed determination, he refused to let go and leave the island in a position of supposed defeat. Finally, a spiritual father of ours, Albie Pearson, was able to get through to Peter and gently persuade him that a move was for the best, at least for now.

Even with the decision made and me working as fast as possible to set our moving plans in motion, it wasn't fast enough. I was desperate to get Peter back to California, so I tried to put him on a flight by himself. That plan failed miserably and things were getting wildly out of hand, so I made yet another desperate call to my father-in-law, John.

John had been our hero more than once. He quickly agreed to make the long journey to be with his son. But before he could complete the five-hour drive to LAX and the flight to Hawaii, Peter went missing.

After my plan to fly Peter off the island failed, my friends Jenny and Sully gave me much a much-needed break by keeping watch over Peter all throughout the night at their rural property. At some point the following day, Peter was delivered home. Exhausted from his restless night, he wanted to take a nap. I was glad for that because sleep always seemed to push the reset button on his mental state.

Later that afternoon, Peter decided to go for a walk. It was only about a mile down the dirt plantation road from our home to Jenny and Sully's property. Informing me that he wanted to walk back to their place, Peter set out on his way while I called my friends to let them know he would be arriving soon. Thankfully, he seemed to be doing better after some rest, as usual.

Not long after Peter headed down the road, a friend stopped by to check in on my husband. Learning that Peter had just left a few minutes prior, Aaron hopped back in his vehicle and told me he'd catch up with him. Aaron had been very much involved in all that had been happening since Peter's affliction first came on, so I was grateful to know that he'd be accompanying him to Jenny and Sully's place. And then I didn't hear anything for a couple of hours. Enjoying a break in the drama and relieved to know that Peter's father would soon arrive, I fell asleep on the couch.

Unfortunately, I later learned that Peter had never made it to Jenny and Sully's property. I gave Aaron a phone call and found out that he'd driven down the road and didn't see any sign of my husband, so he turned around and went home, assuming that Peter had completed the journey ahead of him. It was a total mix-up and now no one knew where Peter was. In full crisis mode, I alerted everyone I could think of that Peter was missing, vulnerable and possibly in danger. With my heart racing, I called the police to inform them of a missing person. They came and, judging by their expressions, took probably the most bizarre report they'd ever heard before heading out in search of Peter. As word spread, more of our friends joined the authorities in the search for my husband. I stayed home with our children in hopes of his possible return. My heart was racing as I paced the floor, scanning the neighborhood from our second floor windows for any sign of him.

Having done all I could do, I now felt completely helpless. As far as I knew, Peter could be lost anywhere amidst the wild, tropical landscape between our home and the nearby northern edge of the island. Perhaps he had walked right past Jenny & Sully's home, on down the dirt road to the one-hundred-foot cliffs. What if he had fallen? Or jumped? We would never find him in the turbulent waters below.

My head swirling with nightmarish possibilities, I literally felt like I would be overcome by panic. People were in and out of my house, our kids were running around, the phone was ringing off the hook, and my mind wouldn't stop. This storm was fierce and threatening to take me out as I struggled to take a deep breath. For all I knew, my husband was already gone.

Suddenly I stopped what I was doing, shut everything and everyone out and walked into my bedroom, closing the door behind me. I couldn't deal with the chaos and tremendous fear any longer. I had to hit the pause button on this madness.

Alone in my room, I stomped my right foot, looked straight up into the heavens and in a yelling whisper demanded, "I need to hear from You *RIGHT NOW!*"

Closing my eyes, I shifted my focus away from everything that felt scary around me. Instantly, my thoughts fell silent and a sensation of liquid peace gently flowed over me from the top of my head to the bottom of my feet. The storm was still there, but I somehow found myself in the calm eye of it now as an inexplicable stillness completely surrounded me.

He's okay.

It came like a soft voice in the wind. Two words, and that was it. Peter was okay. With a fresh assurance in my spirit, I thanked God for answering me, walked out of the room and waited for the good news. I had pressed the pause button, looked beyond my troubled circumstances, refocused on Hope and listened. This moment changed everything for me.

The good news did finally come after five of the longest hours of my life. An officer called to inform me that Peter had been found nearby and taken to our small local hospital as a precaution, but that he seemed to be okay.

Apparently Peter had walked beyond the turn leading to Jenny and Sully's place and kept going down the dirt road a ways, finally entering the nearby home of a stranger. Those five hours, for him, had been wrought with severe mental anguish, stabbing physical pain and tormenting delusions that I could never have dreamed up if I tried.

Then, suddenly, peace came upon him and he seemed to snap out of the entire nightmare in an instant. He left the home he'd unknowingly invaded and ventured back out onto the dirt road. It was there that he was met by the officers who had been searching for him.

By now, Peter's father had landed at the airport in Kona and was relieved to learn of his son's whereabouts. He would arrive at our home on the north side of the island within the hour. Loading the kids up in the car, I raced down to the corner where my friends lived, knowing they'd happily babysit while I hustled over to the hospital. Time was of the essence; I had to get Peter on a plane and off the island with his dad that evening. It felt as though our lives depended on it.

Based on previous experiences we'd had with Peter in hospitals, I knew the chances were good that he'd be placed on an involuntary hold. Hoping to avoid this, I wasted no time in getting him to sign a release and walk out of the hospital with me. He really did seem to be back in his right mind, so away we went.

He was okay, just like the voice said.

John arrived soon after and he and Peter left for the airport in Kona, flying back to the mainland on November fifth, my birthday. Sadly, that was the last day that our family was together on the island. Even still, I was immensely grateful that Peter was once again safe.

Whether or not your personal crisis is as scary as mine was, pressing pause works just the same. Breaking it down into three simple steps, let's take a look at how it's done:

Stop. As you saw in my story here, I had to physically walk into another room—away from the chaos and confusion—and make a conscious effort to press the pause button on the flood of horrifying possibilities attacking my mind. This can be difficult when faced with trauma, but we still have the power to say "ENOUGH!" and press pause.

Look. Look away from the storm and fix your focus on whatever is going to bring you peace in this moment. For me, my focus was shifted from what felt like hell on earth to Heaven above. And that brought me instant peace.

Listen. Quiet your mind. What do you hear? That still small voice, is it whispering to you? What does the Comforter have to say about your situation? Maybe what you need to hear will come in an instant or, perhaps, it will come over time. I've had it happen both ways. The important thing here is that we're tuning out the roar of the wind and the waves and creating space for the voice of Peace to speak.

Whenever you feel yourself being overtaken by grief, by mind games or chaos, pull out this tool. Press pause. Set a healthy boundary for yourself. Once you've intentionally adjusted your perspective, it's then that you can powerfully choose your response and position yourself with Peace despite what's going on around you. Try it out today if, at any point, you begin to feel overwhelmed by whatever situation you might find yourself in.

• • •

It's empowering to

know that we have the

ability to take a time out

whenever we feel

the need for one.

• • •

STAYING PRESENT

· · ·

"Do not anticipate trouble or worry about what
may never happen. Keep in the sunlight."

MARK TWAIN

· · ·

Sprawled out over my daughter's bed, I wept. My children were staying with my parents for the night and, as I walked by their empty
rooms, I was overcome by intense fear and grief. What would happen
to them when I was gone? Their father loved them dearly but, with
his compromised health, how could he possibly raise them well without me? And what if something happened to him as well? Then who
would take them in?

I envisioned each of my children growing up in a world where I no
longer existed, where I was no longer present for the big moments or

the small ones, where I couldn't protect them, hold them or comfort them. And I lost it.

Having been inexplicably sick for months, not one medical doctor had been able to figure out the sources of my various afflictions. The exhaustion, the pain and the uncertainty had taken a toll on me, not to mention the stress of what I had been walking through with Peter for a couple of years by this time.

The bleeding had started again and I was terrified. Blood was scary. Blood meant something was very wrong. Blood meant that something unseen was trying to take me out. My digestive system was failing me. I had seen these exact symptoms in someone I knew who had cancer once. My days were surely numbered.

Nearly hyperventilating, I got up and walked into my bathroom to grab some Kleenex. As I stood there blowing my nose and wiping my eyes, Peter walked in. Perceiving what was going on, he wrapped his large hands around my shoulders and, from thirteen inches above me, looked into my eyes and gave it to me straight.

> *Jen! Get a grip. As far as we know TODAY, you don't have cancer. As far as we know TODAY, you aren't dying anytime soon. As far as we know TODAY, you will see our children grow up far into adulthood. Stay in today. Tomorrow we'll deal with whatever comes. And then we'll do it again the next day. But for now, stay here. Stay present.*

Let's take a collective deep sigh of relief and let that truth sink in for a moment. My husband was right. This was precisely what I needed to hear. I needed someone to grab hold of me and tell me to stop allowing fear to drive my thoughts into a future that likely wouldn't ever happen. And none of the fears I was battling that evening ever did come to fruition. I had worked myself into a near panic attack for nothing.

Author Micca Campbell points out in her book *An Untroubled Heart*, "The truth is, most of what we worry about never comes to pass, but we insist on tormenting ourselves anyway." Isn't that the truth? We *do* torment ourselves all too often. It reminds me of the question Jesus asks his disciples in the book of Luke. "Who of you by worrying can add a single hour to your life?" (Luke 12:25, NIV) So why do we continue to try?

I'm convinced that all of my persistent, irrational worrying through that difficult season in my life only served to exacerbate my health troubles. Even though I wasn't *really* dying, I thought I was. Our brains don't know the difference between a *perceived* threat and an *actual* one. The same stress response occurs. The same stress hormones are released and the same damage is done to our bodies. While the harm we inflict upon ourselves by worrying unnecessarily might be invisible, that doesn't make it any less real.

Do you know that seventy percent of our immune system resides in our gut? That's because our gut is home to trillions of microscopic bugs, or at least that's what I tell my kids. We have the good bugs and the bad bugs. Ideally, we want the bad bugs to stay below fifteen percent of our total gut microbiome. Why does this matter and what does it have to do with worrying about the future?

When we worry, the stress response that takes place in the body subjects our otherwise healthy gut to direct attack. Have you ever heard anyone respond to a dose of bad news by saying that they felt like they got hit in the gut? Well, that description is surely accurate because that's exactly what happens. Stress hits us square in the gut. It doesn't matter if it's mental, emotional, physical or imagined stress, the result is the same.

The balance in the gut bacteria as well as the integrity of the gut lining itself is compromised under prolonged or acute stress. When this occurs, the immune system is weakened and the gut's ability to produce those feel-good, happy hormones such as serotonin is greatly reduced, making it even more difficult to cope with stress. Anxiety and depression waste no time in taking up residence in the absence of sufficient serotonin. Are you beginning to see how this is all connected?

I want to provide you with a little of the science behind what happens when we worry in hopes that this will arm you with good information. For me, personally, I make a greater effort to maintain healthy stress levels when I remember the positive health benefits of doing so. We actively promote mind-body wellness within ourselves when we say no to projecting fear into the future. I'm a living example of this truth.

Do you find yourself preoccupied with worrying about things that may never happen? If so, there's no better day than today to bring this unncessary torment to a halt. Here's a simple exercise that you can do right now. Take a few moments out of your day to identify your most troublesome worries and write them down on a piece of paper. I like to call this a brain dump. Just get it out. All of it. When you can't think of another irrational fear that's been taking up precious real estate in your thoughts, look over your list.

Has anything you see on that paper done you any favors? Is this list adding anything good to your life? I doubt it.

Let's take this list and bid it farewell, shall we? There are lots of ways to do this. You can simply toss it in the trash or, for my eco-friendly friends, recycle it. Burn it. Make a paper airplane or a sailing boat out of it and watch it disappear. However you choose to free yourself from projecting fearful thoughts into your future, make sure that you make a clean break and don't pick it up again. And when those fears *do* try to creep back in—which they *will*—remember Peter's words to me.

Remind yourself as often as you need to that your fears are lying to you, tormenting you, and slowly eroding your immune system. It's time to silence those fears, protect your health, and stay in the present.

• • •

How amazing would it feel to be free of

this imaginary, anxiety-producing future?

The key is to live in today, keep your

thoughts in the present, and trust that

you'll have all the grace you need to deal

with whatever comes tomorrow.

• • •

FILTERING THOUGHTS

• • •

"The greatest weapon against stress is our ability
to choose one thought over another."

WILLIAM JAMES

• • •

Chances are good that most of us have at least one person in our lives who lacks a filter. You know, like the one at the family gathering who seems to have diarrhea of the mouth. And the one you've learned not to share delicate information with because you can count on it being indiscreetly broadcasted to those outside of your inner circle. The one who can't seem to help but externally process every thought that crosses his or her mind out loud.

My husband, Lance, is a man with a well-trained filter. Through his observations of others with less-restrained pie holes, as he likes to call them, he made the decision long ago to lean heavily in the direction of self-restraint. When Lance was admonished as a young boy, "If you don't have anything nice to say, then don't say anything at all," he actually took it to heart. To this day, I sometimes struggle to draw out his raw thoughts if he feels that there's a chance that something might not land in the "nice" category. As much as I prefer to hear what's really going on in that mysterious mind of his, I have to say that I've grown to appreciate his wisdom in being slow to speak or, in some cases, choosing not to speak at all.

So what does this have to do with filtering thoughts? Well, moments before unfiltered thoughts exit our mouths, we consciously or subconsciously choose our thoughts. Those harsh words never would have escaped our mouths had they not first begun as thoughts, even if we didn't realize we were thinking them. Doesn't it seem to make sense that we should then practice the discipline of filtering our thoughts, thus easing the burden of trying to control what begs to fly out of our mouths a fraction of a second later? It only takes a moment of our time, we just have to learn to be intentional about it.

Pausing and asking ourselves a series of questions can help us intentionally filter our thoughts and words alike. I like to call this process "straining my brain." Here are some suggestions:

- Is this thought true?

- Is this thought deserving of my attention?

- Will this thought add value, purpose, or meaning to my life?

- Is this thought truly worth my time and energy?

- Does this thought bring me peace?

- Am I motivated towards excellence by this thought?

- Does this thought inspire me to love others well?

- Are others going to be edified by this thought if it leaves my mouth?

If the answer is yes to any or all of these questions, then it's safe say this particular thought has passed the test and can be allowed in. I'm sure that you could add your own set of inquiries to mine, but this is a good starting point.

When it comes to filtering our thoughts, a good rule to apply comes from the often-quoted verses, Philippians 4:8-9 (NLT).

> *And now, dear brothers and sisters, one final thing. Fix your thoughts on what is true, and honorable, and right, and pure, and lovely, and admirable. Think about things that are excellent and worthy of praise... then the God of peace will be with you.*

Filtering our thoughts as described in the verses above invites peace. This exercise helps us practice what we learned on Day 6 in regards to staying present. When we fail to filter out those thoughts that cause us to spiral into an imagined future filled with fear, peace is forfeited. Staying present requires the constant monitoring and filtering out of thoughts that threaten to derail us.

There were many times when I was walking with Peter through his four-year battle with mental illness that I had to be very intentional about choosing which thoughts I allowed in and which thoughts I sent packing. I would often remind myself, "Just because a thought knocks at the door doesn't mean I have to let it in."

I can't tell you how many times I heard this as a young person growing up in the church. And it's true! When a thought comes knocking at the door of our minds, it usually happens quickly. In that moment, we're faced with an almost subconscious opportunity to welcome a thought in for entertaining or send it away from the doorstep of our mind's gate.

This is a crucial juncture. Thoughts that are allowed in, fed and nurtured will likely decide to take up permanent residence like a stray cat looking for a new home.

Cognitive neuroscientist Dr. Caroline Leaf states that we have twenty-four to forty-eight hours to dismiss a thought before it actually takes a semi-permanent hold within the brain.[1] That hold is only semi-permanent because any thought can be wired out of the brain with proper training. This gives us a short window of time to stand back and make careful observations before granting entrance to a thought pattern that has the potential to harm us.

The ancient Greek philosopher Aristotle is quoted as saying, "It is the mark of an educated mind to be able to entertain a thought without accepting it." And that's exactly what my friend from college, Gwyne, learned in the months following the devastating loss of her baby girl. Had she not learned this important concept of recognizing and disempowering toxic thoughts, she likely would have been ruled by the voice of hopelessness that attempted to steal her joy. (You can read her own account of this journey at the end of the book.)

Turning toxicity away at the door is much easier than laboriously weeding it out months, or possibly years, down the road once it's become well established. The good news is that we DO have this window of opportunity to make powerful choices.

. . .

Today I invite you to enjoy the

peace and sense of mastery that

comes from intentionally choosing

which thoughts you will allow

in and which ones you will send

away from the gate of your mind.

. . .

FEELING PAIN

• • •

"Pain demands to be felt or it will
demand that you feel nothing at all."

ANN VOSCAMP

• • •

I'm not one who likes to cry in front of people. In fact, I avoid it at all costs. When I feel tears bubbling up, I typically do my best to shut them down. If I fail at doing so, I'm basically a hot mess. I can't speak. My face contorts, my chin quivers and my nose runs. It's embarrassing, uncomfortable and makes me feel out of control. I envy those who can successfully pull off a good public messy cry.

A dear friend of mine went through a painful divorce following a traumatic ten-year nightmare of a marriage. She cried each time we spoke during that awful season, but she did so with admirable grace.

It didn't matter that tears streamed down her freckled cheeks, she just kept pouring out her broken heart until she at last got through to the other side of her crisis.

My friend was in immense emotional pain and not afraid to feel it. I recall watching her with wonder. Her ability to be so openly raw gave me the courage to do the same. Her capacity to be so beautifully transparent and freely vulnerable felt like a gift. I knew that she was a safe and compassionate person to go to with my own bitter situation down the road.

I once wrongly believed that emotional resilience looked like keeping my emotions under control. If I could just be strong and keep my feelings at bay long enough to hold it together in front of others, I was winning. As human beings, we are hardwired to avoid pain. And I sure as heck didn't want to allow anyone else to see my pain.

Let's be honest. We'd prefer to dress our pain up, put a pretty shade of lipstick on it and then dismiss it once and for all. In doing so, we sadly invalidate our true feelings and slap unfair judgment upon ourselves. Where's the self-compassion in that? It's only when we can learn to extend to ourselves the kind of compassion we'd expect to receive from a dear friend that we can accept our messy feelings and grow through them. To grow, we first have to allow ourselves to feel.

I'm still not great at showing my most private emotions in front of anyone other than my tenderhearted husband, but I have experienced the freedom found in doing so on more than one occasion. I recall a day when my best efforts to stuff down my painful feelings completely failed in front of one of my dearest friends. It felt like my whole world was blowing up yet again and I was barely holding it together. All I needed to do was keep myself composed long enough to drop my daughter off at my friend Lauren's house and be on my way. I hoped to get in and out as quickly as possible.

Lauren met me in the driveway of her home and, with her characteristically keen intuition and ability to read me like a book, she wasn't going to let me off so easily. She asked how I was doing in a way that required a more authentic response than I was prepared to give. Just having someone ask me this question was enough to put a hefty crack in my armor. My quivering chin couldn't lie. I couldn't keep it in any longer. The dam broke and, before I knew what was happening, I found myself draped over Lauren's shoulder as I stood in her driveway sobbing uncontrollably. Barely intelligible words attempted to communicate how scared and heartbroken I was.

There was no retracting this emotional display of mine now. Both mortified and relieved to have what was once dangerously locked inside of me now on the outside for us both to see, I felt myself breathe an exhausted sigh of relief. My troubled heart was now accessible to some much-needed comfort and healing.

Lauren provided the compassionate, non-judgmental space I needed to bring my buried pain into the light. The tension I hadn't realized I'd been carrying was now gone. Honestly, breaking down had never felt so good. It should probably come as no surprise, then, that Lauren was the first person I instinctively called when I learned of my husband's sudden death a year or so later.

At the time, I didn't really think it through. Calling my friend was a gut reaction. Standing in my front yard in hopes of protecting my five-year-old daughter from the tragic news, I remember how my hands shook as I fumbled through the contacts in my phone for Lauren's number. Subconsciously I knew that I needed someone who could handle sitting with me in my moment of shock and trauma, if only over the phone. Lauren was someone who would be able to connect with my flood of emotions, someone who would feel the pain with me and validate my distress without trying to fix it. I needed permission to be an absolute wreck free from worrying about the listener.

My history with Lauren had taught me that I was drawn to a judgment-free zone like a magnet. I mean, aren't we all? I believe this to be our human nature. We all desperately want to feel unconditionally loved and accepted, secure in spite of our own unique imperfections. Why is it such a struggle for us, then, to create a safe haven within ourselves to feel our darkest emotions without casting judgments? Why do we look at our fear or anxiety and so quickly become angry with ourselves? Why do we feel frustrated when unexpected waves of grief catch us off-guard?

I certainly don't feel frustrated with my kids when their grief resurfaces. Are you kidding me? Nothing floods my heart and brings me to tears more quickly than seeing the pain of devastating loss manifest itself in my children. I want to crawl inside of it with them, squeeze them tight and tell them it's okay to feel their big feelings. I feel it, too. Consider the comfort and freedom we would experience as adults if we were able to extend that same level of permission and compassion to ourselves.

If you're reading this today and you can feel that dam of emotions nearing a tipping point within you, I want to ask you to consider releasing it. If your heart is racing and your breathing is shallow, I'd be willing to guess that you're working hard at keeping those painful emotions under wraps. Have you tried giving yourself permission to feel the pain? Real growth and healing can't come until you're able to acknowledge your feelings and finally feel them.

Instead of rejecting our emotions, let's start by identifying what we're feeling today. For the one feeling anxious, try writing down, "I feel anxious today and that's okay." For the one feeling immobilized by grief, write down, "I feel sad today and that's completely normal." For the one feeling hopelessly discouraged write down, "I feel deeply discouraged, but this won't last forever. This is part of being human." Speak to yourself in the same way that you might imagine yourself speaking to a child feeling the same difficult emotions.

We're all pushing past pain on some level and it takes courage to face our uncensored feelings. Regularly allowing yourself to feel all that rises up within you and calling it by name will help you to cope with your emotions in a healthy way. Otherwise, what you continue to resist will persist until you are ready to be completely free. If this feels overwhelming and scary, please don't hesitate to enlist the help of a professional to guide you through this process. There's no shame in reaching out for support at any stage of the healing experience.

If you feel stuck, the healing process can begin today. Just keep in mind that it is a process and it will take time to unravel those emotions that have been stuffed deep down inside. You don't have to go through that process alone. Today is a first step and that step can't be determined by anyone but you. Are you ready to say yes to healing? Do you want to invite a supportive individual into this journey with you? Perhaps the first step for you looks like giving yourself permission to sit in your feelings or putting a name to those feelings.

• • •

Whatever it is you choose,

be patient and compassionate

with yourself. Embrace the

process, feel the pain and

know that joy is on its way.

• • •

RELEASING PERFECTION

• • •

"When perfectionism is driving...
shame is always riding shotgun."

BRENÉ BROWN

• • •

The irony is not lost on me that I'm sitting down to write on the topic of releasing perfection as I simultaneously battle perfectionism in myself. Each and every day that I move this less-than-perfect book project forward, I fight it. Believe it or not, authoring a real live book has become one of my greatest tests as a recovering perfectionist.

I often joke that my parents must have had spellcheck installed in me when I was born because I've been a natural-born editor for as long as I've been able to hold a pen (yet I still find typos in my own writing all the time). I'm a rule follower and it *really* rubs me the wrong way when others don't follow the rules. Dependable punctuality, creative organization and careful scheduling make my world go 'round (which comes in quite handy in a family of eight, I might add). Nothing quite makes my heart sing like a well-arranged closet or neatly folded stacks of laundry.

In my younger years, these skills came in handy as I created tidy clothing displays at South Coast Plaza in Costa Mesa, California or diligently served the companies I worked for with great attention to detail. My high standards have driven me towards both excellence and success my entire life. While I'm grateful for my God-given abilities, I am also keenly aware of the down-sides of my natural tendencies.

I can still remember the day when I experienced an epiphany concerning my own battle with perfectionism. Up until that day, I had always felt that my drive to achieve perfection in my work was an admirable quality. It wasn't until I was a grown woman that I one day looked around at my chronically messy home and wondered at how a perfectionist like myself could possibly present as such a dichotomy. And then the proverbial light bulb suddenly switched on to expose the true method to my madness.

Although a visitor to my home might have determined otherwise, I actually wasn't a slob and I certainly wasn't lazy. In my head I knew that I was a highly organized person. But what I now realized about myself was that if I didn't have the time and energy to clean my home to my perfectionistic standards, I didn't even want to try. It was all or nothing for me. I'd rather deal with the inconvenience of living in chaos than endure the shame that I knew would come if my best efforts weren't good enough. The most ridiculous part was that no one was ascribing this shame to me but the voices inside my own head.

Since I didn't really want to live in such disorder, I began striking a compromise with myself. I set a timer for as little as ten minutes and completed as much tidying up as I could until the alarm sounded. What I couldn't get done in ten minutes could wait for the next time I had ten available minutes. And I slowly learned to be okay with that. My home may never be so immaculate as your home or the home I grew up in, but that's okay.

This liberating discovery doesn't provide me with a free pass to be a slovenly woman. On the contrary, my home is more tidy and organized today with eight people living in it than it was when my family was half the size. Releasing the goal of perfection freed me up to accept my best as good enough. I think that having a family of eight forced me to finally accept the fact that it's impossible for my home to ever be as neat and tidy as I'd like it to be. You know what they say about when the stalls are empty, the barn is clean. Well, my stalls are far from empty and my barn is never going to be perfectly clean.

Releasing perfectionism doesn't mean giving up on aiming for excellence. It *does* mean giving up on shame, the voice that tries to tell us that nothing we do will ever be good enough. Contrary to what it may seem, perfectionism doesn't actually do us any favors. The goal of perfection doesn't drive us to do better, it drives us into paralysis. If shame had its way, I'd remain stuck in a perpetual cycle of editing and re-editing this manuscript forever because there will *always* be room for improvement.

I know what it's like to be a recovering perfectionist while riding the waves of life's storms. There's nothing quite like a massive disturbance to challenge deeply rooted habits of perfectionism. Those of us who battle with this are also usually the ones who avoid asking for help at all costs. We'd rather suffer in silence than feel like a burden to anyone else. And that's why the storm I weathered with Peter provided unending opportunities for me to release perfection.

There's no possible way that I could handle all that was required of me as a wife and mother of three young children at home while *also* dealing with the stress connected to the situation we found ourselves in. It was too much! As a result, I had to come to terms with the fact that my expectations for myself required a serious adjustment. And not only that, but I had to let people into my messy life.

While one of my biggest fears was having an unexpected visitor show up at my door when my home was unkempt and my hair and make-up undone, I got over that real fast when I was desperate for help. When I was in a crisis, I was suddenly very okay with friends showing up unannounced to help get my seven-year-old ready for his first day of school as I struggled to get out of bed. Even with as uncomfortable as it felt at first, I quickly learned to accept help with getting our trash to the dump or—even more humbling—having our laundry done by hands other than my own.

You were never meant to go through this storm alone, my friend. On the contrary, we are wired to need each other. To even attempt to navigate through this life apart from one another only serves to invite self-sabotage, burnout and the very thing we fear so much—failure. But you are *not* a failure just because it feels like your life has been derailed at the moment. We all go through these times; it's part of the human experience.

Is perfectionism holding you hostage, preventing you from receiving the support you so urgently need right now? If so, let's decide today to expose perfectionism for what it really is and release it entirely. Perfectionism is not your friend. On the contrary, perfectionism is toxic. Perfectionism is only "fear of judgment" and "fear of failure" cloaked in a seemingly harmless word like "perfect." Perfectionism will tell you that you're never ready, you're never good enough, you'll never know enough. It threatens to prevent you from ever starting or finishing anything well. Perfectionism is debilitating, driving us to overwork ourselves to the point of self-harm. Are we ready to kick this thing to the curb already?

We aren't going to overcome perfectionism overnight. It takes time and practice to change the way we've always done things and even longer to change the way we think about ourselves. Perfectionism is a trap that seeks to keep us isolated in a prison of never-good-enough. You and I both know that we can't afford to live in isolation even if it does offer some attractive (however empty) promises. In my personal experience, inviting the right people into my crisis was more likely to earn their unconditional love, trust and respect rather than the much-dreaded judgment that I feared.

As you go about your day today, celebrate your accomplishments. Maybe you got out of bed this morning and took care of your kids even though your heart feels broken or your body is failing you. That's worth celebrating! Who cares if you went to bed with dishes in the sink? Perfectionism wants to tell us that we're unworthy and inadequate all day long. We can silence those voices by honoring the fact that pushing past our pain every single day qualifies us as overcomers.

I'm not writing from a position of having mastered the subject matter. You'd better believe that I'm more than a little anxious about releasing this book for the world to scrutinize. I know that far more talented writers than myself are likely to pick up my work and find all sorts of mistakes or ways that it could have been better. But I can't let that stop me from getting my message out. Those who may judge my work will hopefully be far outnumbered by those who will be blessed by it in some way. And that's what I have to choose to focus on.

What I want to encourage you to do today is decide what you will focus on. Will you focus on what you have overcome and accomplished or on what perfectionism wants you to believe about yourself? Will you focus on your perceived inadequacies or on your hard-earned victories?

• • •

Rather than listen to the lie that

you'll never be good enough,

I invite you to release perfection and

embrace the empowering truth that

who you are is already enough.

• • •

CRACKING A SMILE

• • •

"Smile, it's free therapy."

DOUGLAS HORTON

• • •

If you happen to be a runner, I tip my proverbial hat to you. I've tried to be a runner several times. Really, I have. From trail running, treadmills, and running apps that promise to take me from the couch to a 5K in six weeks, I've tried it all to no avail. I don't know what I'm doing wrong, but I just can't bring myself to enjoy this form of ~~self-torture~~ exercise.

While I enjoy my brisk walks along the trails surrounding our neighborhood, I observe people running by me carrying on actual conversations. Yes, they can talk *and* run at the same time. This astounds me. All I can manage when I attempt to run is thinking about the fact that I'm running (okay, so jogging) and wondering when the pain will end!

I've long since surrendered my running shoes and, to this day, the runner's high eludes me. To get around this, I've found a way to achieve essentially the same thing, minus all the physical exertion, sweat and desperate gasps for oxygen. This may seem a little like cheating, but it works. It's free, completely legal and requires absolutely no running at all. You can do it anywhere, anytime. The only caveat is that it *is* highly contagious. Are you ready for it?

SMILE! Yep, that's it. The simple act of smiling releases the same happy hormones that are responsible for the much acclaimed runner's high. These hormones, otherwise known as endorphins, are responsible for the sense of accomplishment and euphoria that runners seem to enjoy. (Or so they say.)

We've already talked a little about the power we possess to choose which mood-altering chemicals our brains will release. Choosing positive thought patterns when we're not feeling positive at all can sometimes take a bit of effort. On paper it sounds easy enough, but I know how it is when you're really going through it and you just can't bring yourself to think a happy thought. In that case, cracking a smile is our best bet.

Now let's be real. When I find myself a bit bogged down in life, I'm not one to naturally wear an easy smile. While it feels as though the weight of the world is resting upon my shoulders, I feel it in my face. I don't want to smile. Smiling seems to betray me, communicating that I'm okay with the way things are when that isn't actually the case at all. As a transparent person, forcing a smile feels inauthentic. I'd much prefer to maintain the resting face of a frowning bulldog if that feels more true to me at the time.

During times like these, I have to consciously remind myself why I *need* to smile even when I don't feel like it. Smiling becomes a deliberate decision, something I do because it's good for me and not because I feel like it. Smiling really is free therapy. Allow me to share with you both the why and the how of what I'll refer to as "smile therapy" from here on out.

Smiling has a way of tricking our brains into thinking everything's A-OK, even if it's not. But why would we want to force it? Well, because our goal throughout this book is to find ways to bring our mindsets and our physical bodies back into healthy balance. The simple act of cracking a smile is one easy tool we can use to advance us towards our goal.

With our thoughts and emotions governing much of what occurs in our brain chemistry, we have the ability to initiate various physiological changes in our bodies. Remember the imaginary vacation we took together on Day 1? We learned that envisioning a vacation provides us with the same health benefits as an actual vacation. Our brains don't know the difference. And the same is true for smiling. Fabricating a smile works as well as the real thing.

Those happy hormones I've mentioned called endorphins (short for endogenous morphine) are neurotransmitters released by our brains. Neurotransmitters are basically little chemical messengers that our bodies produce to perform vital functions. The heart pumps blood, we breathe, and we digest our food because our chemical messengers are working for us even as we sleep.

Endorphins are a specific type of neurotransmitter that cause happy feelings, providing us with an overall sense of wellbeing. By smiling, we trigger the release of these merry chemicals by the movement of the muscles in our faces. Each time we smile, our brain is upstairs enjoying a joyful party that informs our mental, emotional and physical bodies that life is just grand, even if it isn't.

The positive benefits of endorphins are far-reaching and can last for up to twelve hours. For one, taking note of the name "endogenous morphine" clues us in to the fact that endorphins are natural painkillers. Our own bodies provide us with the means to block the perception of pain through purely organic means.

Other benefits provided by a healthy dose of endorphins include lower blood pressure, decreased anxiety levels, increased immune function, the release of trapped emotions and, of great importance, the reduction of the damaging stress hormone, cortisol. Cortisol is bad news on many levels and is also largely responsible for stress-induced weight gain. Maybe we could also find a way to smile ourselves skinny? Just a thought.

For my dear readers who are genuinely down in the dumps, I want to speak directly to you for a moment. Please remember that I've spent a great deal of time sitting in physical and emotional pain myself and the last thing I want to do is make light of your current situation. When life is scary or difficult or just plain traumatic, smiling is not what we feel like doing. It's okay if that's where you're at. I have something for you to try. To do this, all you need is a pencil. *Yes, a pencil.*

Go ahead, find a pencil. Now place the pencil between your teeth with the lead point and the eraser facing in opposite directions from the corners of your mouth. The pencil should be resting horizontally across your tongue. Now softly bite down and hold it there. Look in the mirror. Are you smiling now?

Holding a pencil between your teeth in this manner forces the muscles in your face to mimic a smile. Again, it doesn't matter that you're not smiling because you think life is awesome. What does matter is that the movement of the muscles in your face are triggering the release of the feel-good hormones you desperately need right now.

If you've ever attended one of my workshops or a conference I've spoken at, then you've probably experienced the silliness of sitting in a room full of people simultaneously biting down on pencils. I'm guilty of making everyone in the room participate in this exercise because I want to demonstrate that it really works. Because it does!

Just this week I found myself in need of a serious mood adjustment. Thankfully, my trusty pencil was available just to the right of my driver's seat in the car. I placed it in position and continued down the road until I felt better. And I *did* feel better by the time I returned home. Sounds silly, right? I know. But I've been employing this goofy tool for about the last five years through anything ranging from a slight case of the Mondays to the sudden loss of my husband. I'm telling you, it works. Go ahead and try it for yourself.

We all have our days when we wake up and don't feel much like getting out of bed. I know that I have mornings when I dread the routine of another draining day. Or perhaps I feel sad and discouraged about something relating to one of our kids. On those mornings I have to choose to snap out of it and shift my mindset. Smiling helps me do that. I will literally lay in bed with my head on my pillow, look up at the ceiling and force my entire face into a smiling position until I feel the heaviness lift.

Combining smile therapy with mentally and spiritually releasing whatever threatens to weigh you down does wonders for the psyche. Visualizing worries being traded in for peace while also enjoying an infusion of happy hormones in the brain is a winning combination.

• • •

Putting this simple tool into practice

unlocks a mindset shift from gloomy

and full of dread to sunny and hopeful

in a matter of minutes. I encourage you

to try it out for yourself and begin

incorporating this new tool into your

daily life whenever you need a boost.

• • •

LEARNING TO LAUGH AGAIN

• • •

"Laughter is part of the human survival kit."

DAVID NATHAN, COMEDIAN

• • •

There were lots of times when what our family was suffering through together felt like a lead blanket over our home. While Peter had always been a bit of a class clown, relishing in any opportunity to spark a good laugh, his illness sucked the joy out of him during the last few years of his life. He didn't smile or laugh quite like he used to.

This was one of the many changes that caused him to seem like an entirely different person from the Peter I'd always known. He would often go through periods of intense heaviness that he struggled to snap out of. It was in the midst of one of these times that we had an opportunity to speak with a pastor following a Sunday morning service.

During this conversation, Pastor Kris Vallotton patiently listened to Peter describe the intensity of all he had been experiencing and mulling over in his overactive mind. Peter was carrying on about some deep revelations he'd been contemplating which, in my opinion, were heavily influenced by his confused mental state. I recall feeling a little embarrassed and had to resist the temptation to interrupt him. Pastor Kris had spoken with us before and understood what was going on, so I left the direction of our conversation up to him. He showed Peter great kindness and simply listened to what he had to say.

When Peter had finished, Pastor Kris nodded but wisely didn't speak directly to anything he had heard. Instead, he looked at Peter and responded with some unexpected advice. "I want you to laugh for thirty minutes every day. Watch a funny movie, listen to my sermons (tongue in cheek), do whatever it is you need to do to laugh each day. Do this together with your wife and your kids."

This was not the response we had expected. Honestly, knowing how direct and unfiltered Pastor Kris can be at times, I actually thought he might challenge Peter's thinking. Instead, Kris wisely chose not to argue with Peter at all. But rather he encouraged him to do the one thing that could break through the intensity of Peter's relentless thought life. He counseled us to laugh together as a family.

How did Pastor Kris know to make a recommendation such as this to someone in Peter's state of mind? Well, probably because he had been in a similar place himself at one time. Pastor Kris has been open about his battle with immobilizing depression a number of years ago. I'm certain, now, that laughter must have been one of the tools he employed regularly to get through that difficult season.

Peter did heed Pastor Kris' advice, thankfully. In fact, he seemed to be empowered by the idea of taking on this new assignment. He looked forward to it. He enjoyed shifting the atmosphere of our home by introducing laughter each day. Whether it was by turning on an episode of America's Funniest Home Videos with the kids, watching our favorite comedians (such as Brian Regan or Jim Gaffigan) on Netflix, engaging in a tickle war or playing one of his infamous pranks on yours truly, our kids were always delighted to participate in any form of comic relief. Laughter has a magical way of bonding us closer to the ones we share it with.

Thanks to Pastor Kris, this new family habit of ours carried us through the many dark days that would follow. Even our children began initiating this comical therapy on their own. My memories of laughing with Peter and the kids through this terribly difficult season are now some of my favorite and most cherished recollections. And the laughter didn't stop even through our time of grieving the loss of Peter. This became one of the greatest lessons I took away from this terribly stressful season of my life. Laughter truly is the best medicine.

Let's take a look at some of the physiological and emotional benefits of laughter: [1,2]

- Reduced muscle tension

- Lower respiratory rate

- Decreased blood pressure

- Increased endorphins

- Reduced emotional stress

- Strengthened immune system

- Elevated mood

- Stabilized blood sugar levels

- Decreased inflammation in the body

- Exercised heart, lungs, diaphragm and abdominal muscles

- Improved alertness

- Diminished depression and anxiety

Similar to laughter, crying also offers many physical and emotional advantages. During times of grief, it's not uncommon to find ourselves bouncing back and forth between laughter and tears. And, as paradoxical as that may seem, it's totally normal. Both laughing and crying accomplish basically the same thing. Laughter and tears alike release emotions we may be holding in, with or without realizing it. I once heard it said that stuffing our emotions down is like burying something that's alive. It doesn't really go away. At some point, those emotions will need to be processed and released.

If I could encourage you to make one small change in your life today, it would be this. Whether it comes in the form of a smile forced by a pencil between your teeth or a good, hearty belly laugh, turn that frown upside down! Exercising your facial muscles for even small increments of time each day is going to make it that much easier to continue making positive steps through whatever challenging circumstances you may be facing.

...

Let laughter be your warfare today

as you laugh in the face of adversity.

I believe you'll be amazed at the level

of breakthrough you'll achieve in

a surprisingly short amount of time.

...

PRACTICING GRATITUDE

• • •

"Create the habit of gratitude and
watch your life transform."

ROBIN LEE

• • •

You might be surprised to learn how my son, Aaron, and I ended the day on June 2, 2014, the day Peter passed away. After our friends and family had gone home, I was alone with my kids for the night. Alyma, age five, had the flu at the time and crashed out early in the evening. Alex, age ten, had returned from spending the evening with close friends and opted to unwind by enjoying a warm shower.

Six-year-old Aaron had chosen to spend the latter part of the day in the comforting company of his best friend, Jack, and was now home and resting in his top bunk. I couldn't help but crawl up there and snuggle him as closely as possible. If I could have squeezed him tight enough to heal his shattered little heart, I would have.

Holding him in my arms, I asked a careful question. "Aaron, what are you grateful for today?" His response: "Well, Mommy, I'm grateful that Daddy got to go to Heaven, that he's having fun there, and that you're my mom." Did your heart just melt as completely as mine did in that moment hearing his response?

Aaron didn't find it strange at all for me to ask him this question on such a sad day because it was our routine. This was the question I'd been asking each of my children every night at bedtime for over a year. He quickly shared three things he was grateful for that evening because he'd already been trained to recognize that, even on our worst days, we *always* have something to be grateful for. Always. And the day that he lost his daddy was no different.

I have to admit, I did hesitate before I presented this question to Aaron, wondering if it was too much to ask of a small child experiencing unimaginable loss. In the end, I went with what I knew instead of how I felt. Our sudden loss didn't take away our choice to practice gratitude. Our pain didn't need to interrupt our nightly ritual. Gratitude still possessed the same power to fortify us as it had for months and years leading up to this traumatic event. To this day, that is still one of my favorite mommy moments.

Upon learning of his father's death, Aaron said that he felt like his heart was going to explode from the devastating pain. And understandably so. He had every right to a free pass from feeling grateful for anything at all that day. I didn't feel like being grateful much myself. But because the habit of practicing gratitude had already been wired into Aaron's brain, it didn't seem to be a choice he had to make. His gratitude came automatically and without pause. Habits are powerful and this is a perfect example of a positive habit in action. I'll never forget what a gift Aaron's simple demonstration of gratitude was to me that day. I felt comforted in knowing that he would be okay.

I had begun practicing gratitude with my children daily as a result of my learning about the power of gratitude during my studies at the Institute for Integrative Nutrition in 2012. Peter passed away in June of 2014, so by that time our gratitude ritual had become well-established. After growing tired of how heavy and discouraging our days felt most of the time, I came to realize how vital it was for us to make gratitude a central part of our lives. I grew to love hearing my children's responses each evening at bedtime. Sometimes they were silly and sometimes they were downright mind-blowing, challenging me to dig deeper in my own attitude of gratitude.

Regardless of what the circumstances of our lives may be, there is always something to be grateful for. And just as there will always be someone having a better day or a better life than we are, there are many more people experiencing worse days and even worse lives. It's all a matter of putting things in perspective. Practicing gratitude helps me to remember that.

Sure, when we're walking through something that feels really difficult, it can be challenging to avoid getting caught up in that. We may feel that we have the right to sit in our negative emotions and let everyone around us know how life has been cruel or unfair. Well, I hate to say it, but trials in life don't make us special or unique. Rather, they make us just like everyone else on the planet. And for most of us, we have it better than we realize even on our worst days. We really do have so many reasons to be thankful.

There are lots of ways to implement a daily gratitude ritual in our lives. When my children were younger, bedtime provided a natural space for us to share what we were grateful for. Now that the kids are a little older, Lance and I have incorporated gratitude into our evening mealtime as a family. We sit around the table with five of our children most nights of the week, pausing to speak a blessing over our meal and over our family. This is one way we've both grown up giving thanks and a tradition we choose to carry on.

Another way we focus on gratitude at mealtime is by going around the table and sharing at least one good thing that happened that day. I've grown to look forward to this time of connecting with our children in this way. Rather than spending our mealtime harping on the kids about their manners or listening to more complaining than we'd like to, we're instead participating in the act of practicing gratitude as a family. We're celebrating the good in our lives and celebrating one another in the process.

I don't know how I would have walked through all that I have without making gratitude a regular discipline in my life. We each have the opportunity to be powerful despite our life's circumstances, to shift our focus from all that seems to be going wrong to what is going well. How you choose to practice gratitude is up to you. Whether you speak it, write it or think it, immerse yourself in thankfulness.

...

Gratitude truly holds the power to

transform mindsets. This seemingly

small shift in your thinking will break

the victim mentality and unleash

the mighty overcomer within you.

...

JOURNALING

• • •

"Gratitude bestows reverence, allowing us to encounter everyday epiphanies, those transcendent moments of awe that change forever how we experience life and the world."

JOHN MILTON

• • •

Making gratitude an integral part of our daily lives can be done in many ways. Sharing what we're grateful for together with our loved ones at a regular time is just one way to foster thankfulness in our hearts and minds. If you come from a family of faith as I do, then giving thanks prior to partaking in a meal might already be a daily habit of yours. But let's not stop there.

In an article on the science behind thankfulness in The Washington Post, reporter Colby Itkowitz states:

Gratitude is too good to be left at the Thanksgiving table. I believe that gratitude is the best approach to life. When life is going well, it allows us to celebrate and magnify the goodness. When life is going badly, it provides a perspective by which we can view life in its entirety and not be overwhelmed by temporary circumstances.[1]

Whether life is going well or not-so-well for you right now, one tool that is guaranteed to add a whole new level of richness to your life is a gratitude journal. I have utilized this not only in my own personal life but also with my health coaching clients. My experience has convinced me that everyone can benefit from utilizing a gratitude journal. This simple practice is life-changing for those who are disciplined enough to be consistent with it. I want to pass along to you what I have shared with my clients over the years about incorporating this healthy habit into your life.

We've probably all tried our hands at journaling at some point in our lives. I know that I have boxes of journals from throughout my life and Peter was an avid journaler as well. The concept of journaling might seem elementary because it is familiar to most of us, but what I want to spell out for you here goes beyond basic journaling. So please hang in there with me while I lead you step-by-step through the process of beginning your own gratitude journal.

- **Choose your journal.** If you don't already possess one that you'll look forward to seeing every day, then I recommend that you treat yourself to a journal that will serve this purpose. You can purchase one you like off the shelf or create your own if you're artistically inspired to do so. Whatever you decide to do, make it your own. Personalize it. This book of your choosing is going to dwell in a conspicuous place for the foreseeable future.

- **Write in your own hand.** I suggest that you try a good old-fashioned handwritten journal for a while. There's something about journaling in your own hand that allows you to slow down and really get in touch with your deepest feelings, thoughts and ideas. Also, hand writing anything at all increases the brain's ability to retain the information.

- **Select a time and place.** Decide when and where you'll establish this new habit. You're going to want to tie this gratitude practice to a regular time or pre-established habit in your day. Do you drink tea or coffee every morning? Perhaps that might be a good time to write in your journal. Do you have a regular break in your day, such as at work or school? Might that be a good time to pause and express your gratitude?

- **Determine your frequency.** Ideally, this needs to become a daily habit. If you really want to up the ante, you can opt for twice a day. Again, this is where implementing a journaling routine upon waking and going to bed at night makes this a natural part of your daily rhythm.

- **Start writing.** At the top of the page, write the date followed by three to five points of gratitude. These can be bullet points, complete sentences or even paragraphs. My suggestion is to keep it simple in the beginning. Once your new habit is established, you can expand upon it to your heart's content.

- **Make it specific.** My kids would often repeat the same gratitude points each night. "I'm grateful for my mom." "I'm grateful for my teacher." "I'm grateful for God." My response to my kids would be, "That's great that you're thankful for your teacher. What about your teacher are you grateful for?" Likewise, in my own journal, I could write, "I'm grateful for my husband." But an even better entry would be, "I'm grateful for the way my husband patiently listens to me, causing me to feel heard and loved." Now I've made it really personal and my heart is swelling with gratitude for Lance with each handwritten word.

- **Be consistent.** There will be days when you just don't feel like writing anything down. Perhaps you're tired or you've had a rough day. Maybe you don't feel ready to let those negative emotions go. This is your opportunity to rise to the gratitude challenge. Despite how you feel in that moment, get out your journal and flip it open. Read over some of your past entries. Take note of how many days you've written in your journal to date. Is how you're feeling in this moment worth breaking your healthy habit for?

- **Personalize it.** As journaling becomes a regular part of your daily life, have fun with it. Add inspirational quotes, happy doodles or pictures of special moments to your journal. There are no rules or limits to what you can do with this. Keep up with the basics as I outlined above, but try branching out as well. I'm sure you'll find ways to use your journal that I've never even thought of before.

There really is no better way to begin and end a day, in my opinion, than meditating on all that we have to be grateful for. Journaling what we're grateful for doesn't negate the fact that perhaps something awful really did happen on any given day. It's okay to be heartbroken *and* grateful in the same moment. In fact, gratitude is a powerful tool for navigating our way through grief.

Today I encourage you to pull up your bootstraps, get out your pen and put it to paper. Surely you can find at least three things to be thankful for even on the hard days. This is one of those times when you need your gratitude practice most, whether you feel like it or not. In fact, this is your opportunity to apply a positive mindset to what feels like a bad day. Sometimes it just takes a little shift in our focus to pull out of a negative mindset.

• • •

The act of journaling has the

ability to carry you past your

anxieties, through painfully

tangled emotions and into a mindful

state of peace and gratefulness.

• • •

EXPRESSING APPRECIATION

• • •

"Abundance grows from the seed of every thank you."

ROBIN LEE

• • •

Recently I took notice of a post my friend Stephanie made on Facebook about expressing gratitude. She shared that something she enjoyed doing was writing notes to people about how much she appreciated them. She pointed out that, "Not only did it brighten their day, but it brightened mine too." Isn't it interesting how that works? Expressing appreciation is a form of practicing gratitude that benefits both the giver *and* the receiver. Everyone wins.

It's easy to become consumed with our own lives when our circumstances feel overwhelming. Unfortunately, this limits our ability to see what's going on beyond ourselves, particularly in the lives of those around us. We can become dangerously self-absorbed and isolated when our eyes are fixed on all that is wrong or difficult. In this un-healthy frame of mind we are more likely to fall prey to depression, anxiety and a sense of hopelessness. We will probably fail to notice, let alone appreciate, the people we have been blessed to share life with. But don't worry, there is a sure way to turn this around.

Expressing sincere gratitude to others helps us to feel happier and more fulfilled. In order to do this, we must intentionally choose to get out of our own heads. Appreciating others requires us to set our self-absorbed mindsets aside long enough to take notice of all that is deserving of our gratitude around us.

Who doesn't feel uplifted after receiving a dose of unexpected ad-miration? I'm pretty sure we all do. And when we choose to offer encouragement to someone else, the act backfires in the best way. We, in turn, feel encouraged simply by knowing that our written or spoken words are making a difference in the life of someone we care about. We reap the rewards of those beneficial happy hormones be-ing released by our brains simply because we took the time to express our appreciation to another.

Remember that our overall goal is to flourish in the midst life's hard-ships, whatever they may be. Anything that we can do to enrich our lives and the lives of those we're connected to will bring us closer to reaching this goal. Rather than continuing to focus on how difficult our situation feels right now or how unjustly we've been treated, we can instead look for ways to express heart-felt appreciation for the people who touch our lives in positive ways. So let's talk about some ways to do that.

The people who are most often overlooked where appreciation is concerned are the ones who most likely reside within the walls of our own homes—our family members. When's the last time you let your spouse know how much you appreciate him or her? And if you're not married, how about the closest person to you? Do they know how much they mean to you? You might know how much you appreciate them, but do they hear it?

About a month ago I decided to be more intentional about letting Lance know what I appreciate about him. To do this, I created a reminder for myself to send him a quick e-mail expressing three things that I appreciated about him every afternoon at two o'clock. I came to look forward to the daily exercise, that moment in my day when I paused to reflect on the many ways my husband blesses our family. My heart swelled with gratitude and affection for him each time I hit the send button on my daily e-mail. A covering of appreciation for this man I've chosen to join my life with overshadowed the petty things that I can sometimes allow to get under my skin.

This is just one example of being intentional about communicating our gratitude directly to someone special in our lives. It's all too easy to fall into complacency in our relationships with those closest to us. We forget to tell them what we love and appreciate about them as time goes on. It's amazing how much more connected and appreciative we truly are to one another when this habit is put into practice.

A similar idea can be applied to our relationships with our children as well. If you have kids, you probably know which ones would best receive your appreciation in handwritten form and which ones would like to hear you speak it to them. Understanding the love languages of our children and communicating to them based on their preferred love languages will ensure that our words of praise are received in a meaningful way. But let's not allow ourselves to get hung up on choosing the perfect vehicle of delivery. The important thing is that we *are* delivering our sincere expressions of gratitude.

With six of our children still living with us, Lance and I certainly understand how challenging it can be at times to verbalize heartfelt appreciation to each child. But let me tell you, taking the time to do so creates a wonderful ripple effect within a home. Everyone feels like a more valued part of the family when they regularly receive a verbal pat on the back. We also feel better about ourselves as parents when we stop to look our children in the eyes and communicate what we appreciate about them. And the common misbehaviors we often see in our children tend to drop off in an environment where they feel seen, heard, and unconditionally treasured.

The same concept can be applied to the workplace or anywhere you have influence. Letting employees, coworkers or friends know that we appreciate who they are and what they add to our lives is powerful. Recognize what life might be like without a certain individual and you'll see that what they add to your life will instantly become more clear.

As you go about your day today, look for opportunities to brighten the world of someone else on some level. Instead of being wrapped up in what's going wrong in your own life, shift your focus to what's going right in your relationships with others.

• • •

Whether through a random act

of kindness towards a stranger or

a heartfelt letter written to a loved

one, find a way to affect someone

else's life in a positive way. You'll be

rewarded with a sense of greater joy

in your own life for having done so.

• • •

INVITING VULNERABILITY

• • •

"The intention and outcome of vulnerability is trust,
intimacy and connection. The outcome of oversharing is distrust,
disconnection—and usually a little judgment."

BRENÉ BROWN

• • •

Yesterday I enjoyed the opportunity to have lunch with a friend of mine who, along with her husband, chose to build their family through the gift of adoption. As an adoptive mother myself, I could quickly recognize that the honeymoon period was over and she was now sitting in some very real feelings. The long-term commitment to these children she didn't bring into the world from her own womb had sunk in. She willingly gave up her former life of independence not to meet her own needs, but because she and her husband saw a real need and rose up to meet it. This is just one of the many reasons why I have so much respect for them.

As my friend and I shared back and forth about our struggles and strategies as mothers, I heard her express a degree of regret for having chosen this life of motherhood. Her new role is tough and requires greater levels of sacrifice than she had anticipated. She misses the freedom of her old life and feels the sting of reality; that freedom is gone for a good, long while. The little people in her life now require all that she and her husband have to give.

Following our time together, I thought about our conversation. My friend had been so real, so candid and so transparent about her feelings as an adoptive mother. I wasn't shocked at all by her admission of feeling both incredibly blessed and a tad regretful at times. On the contrary, I felt a little like standing up and shouting, "YES!" because I knew that she was experiencing absolutely normal emotions that often accompany adoption and she was brave enough to say so.

Parenting is a great challenge in and of itself. Adoption usually provides a whole new set of challenges that we don't hear much about because the parents are too ashamed to speak openly about it. So when I witnessed my friend opening a window into her heart and making herself vulnerable before me, I felt like I'd been handed a gift. She took a risk in communicating her raw thoughts to the likes of me, a mother with seventeen years of parenting experience under my belt. I could have looked down my nose in judgment at her for even hinting at missing her pre-motherhood life, but of course I didn't.

I'd be willing to bet that, if we're completely honest, most of us who are parents know exactly how my friend was feeling; she was just courageous enough to say it. If my friend had come to me and painted a perfect picture of the huge shift she's experienced in her family, I would have been skeptical. In fact, I likely would have had trouble connecting with her because something would not seem quite right. I *expect* a new mom, particularly an adoptive mom, to experience every emotional color of the rainbow.

In her choice to be authentic over lunch together, my friend extended an invitation to be vulnerable that was so refreshing to me. She didn't attach her self-worth as a new mom to her roller coaster of perfectly normal misgivings. I didn't judge her in the least, but instead I felt that she proved her trustworthiness to me in her ability to expose her true self. In return, I was equally able to communicate on a fully genuine level about my own challenges.

I'm not one who typically struggles with demonstrating vulnerability. If anything, I feel that I might need to learn to be a little *less* vulnerable with certain people, the ones I've come to expect judgment from. You know who they are in your own life. I realize that not everyone is ready for the raw exchanges that I crave. But for those of you who can show up and be seen for who you *really* are and what you're *really* going through, I want to be your friend. And I'm certain there are lots of others who want to be your friend, too. The world needs more brave, authentic people!

Vulnerability can feel particularly scary when we're in a tough situation that we fear others might not understand. I felt a lot of that through all I walked through with Peter. Ours was a situation so uniquely difficult and nearly impossible to explain, I had to come to grips with the fact that others would likely judge me out of their own lack of information and experience. That was tough for me because

I'm one who *really* likes to feel understood and seen in what I feel is an accurate light. The problem was, no one else was actually walking in my shoes but me. No one else was living my life day-in, day-out. People could try to imagine what my life was like, but they couldn't really know like I did. And so I learned to be very careful about who I was open with. Even still, I found myself in a position of being misjudged and even falsely accused on a regular basis.

Feeling connected to others is vital as we navigate our way through the ups and downs of life. In the absence of vulnerability, we won't find those necessary connections. If you prefer to maintain superficial relationships, that's precisely what you'll achieve when you allow fear to squelch opportunities to be real and authentic with those who care about you. Becoming a person who is comfortable with vulnerability doesn't mean that you have to expose yourself for all to see. There should be at least a select few in your life that you can go to in raw form without having to worry about them judging you. If you don't feel that you have anyone safe to go to, this might be a good space for a professional to fill until you do make those important connections with others in your life.

We all have our own unique struggles and weaknesses, some more traumatic and life-altering than others. Ideally we would learn to accept this about ourselves and one another. You don't have to be strong all the time and neither do I. It's okay to allow others to see that we are as human and broken as the next person. While you might fear that people will see your pain and turn away, I suspect that the opposite might be true. Nothing makes a person more attractive to me than raw vulnerability.

Genuine authenticity might feel awkward and uncomfortable at first, but I believe you'll find that others are attracted to the beauty of your accessible heart. If you don't have relationships in your life that you consider to be deep and fulfilling, I encourage you to give vulnerability a try.

• • •

You'll be surprised not only by

how much better you feel when

you're able to connect with others on

a real level, but by the increase in

intimacy you'll enjoy with those

you choose to be open with.

• • •

DISCOVERING COMMUNITY

• • •

"The need for connection and community is primal, as
fundamental as the need for air, water and food."

DR. DEAN ORNISH

• • •

There are no words to sufficiently describe how very painful it was for
me to leave my friends in Hawaii when I made the decision to move.
The tears spill out even now when I think of it. It felt like a big joke on
me, a cruel tease. I got to experience real community long enough to
never want to live without it again. The deeply interconnected life I
had lived with friends that had become my family there on the island
bonded our hearts together in such a way that it thoroughly broke me
to say good-bye. When I left Kohala, leaving my island tribe behind
felt like the rug was being pulled right out from underneath me.

In the absence of my Kohala ohana, I felt completely lost. (*Ohana* = family) What my own family had experienced in our last few months on the island was totally devastating and our dear ohana lived through that scary time with us. Although they didn't understand what was happening any more than we did, they only showed us exceptional kindness and love. There was no replacing these people.

Now back in Redding, I was faced with the reality of either living a disconnected life or attempting to start over and re-create a sense of community for myself. It was true that no one would ever really understand us like the ones we'd left behind on the island, but I knew that I couldn't continue to walk through our ongoing trial apart from a community who knew me and saw what we were going through.

It wasn't long after moving to Redding that I first met my friend Lauren, the one I mentioned earlier in my story about having a meltdown in her driveway. This was a pivotal moment for me. Even though Lauren was a new friend, I instantly knew that she was a kindred spirit. Soon we were walking to one another's homes, showing up comfortably unannounced at times, and even sharing in a holiday meal together with our families at Eastertime. This was beginning to feel like a little taste of the life I loved so much back in Hawaii. My friendship with Lauren brought me the first glimmer of hope I'd seen since our sudden move back to my hometown.

My connection with Lauren soon led to other connections as she introduced me to her friends and, before long, we had formed a home group consisting of wellness-minded moms just like us. We started out down a road towards renewed health together, sharing our knowledge, experience and delicious healthy food along the way. This was during the time when my own health crisis was in full swing. I gleaned as much as I could from these women each time we met, applying their wisdom to my areas of physical and emotional brokenness.

I made the choice early on to be completely vulnerable and share as much as I could about where I was at and what I'd been through with these ladies, most of them strangers at first. Desperate to feel known and supported again, I knew that if I was going to truly prosper where I was planted, I had to fully let them in. At one point I actually wrote my new home group friends a letter to explain what had happened to our family in Hawaii. It felt too overwhelming to try to describe it in person at the time. I just needed them to understand where I was coming from.

Little did I know that this home group would become my place of refuge and primary source of emotional support for the next five years. Just as our Kohala ohana lived through the onset of Peter's illness with us and all of the trauma associated with that, my home group walked closely with me through those painful last few years of Peter's life as well as his sudden passing. Whenever I found myself at my wit's end (which was often), I was able to call on them. I'm sure they grew tired of the ongoing drama in my life at times, but there wasn't really anything I could do to make it stop. They were my sounding board, my prayer network, my "homies," and the ones who did thoughtful things like placing a beautiful bouquet of flowers at my door on my first Valentine's Day without Peter.

It's a great challenge to find community like this in our culture today. In Kohala, most of us lived within walking distance of one another. There was one community park, one main local grocery store and only one or two options for school. Because of this, our lives intersected naturally every single day. This made it easy to do life together.

In most places it takes a great deal of intentionality and sacrifice to be part of one another's lives. It's all too easy to disappear into the fabric of busyness woven into a culture where there is so much talk about living in community, but oftentimes little evidence of it. And since I can't gather up all of my favorite people and whisk them away to share life together in my favorite spot on the Big Island, I—like you—must choose to create a sense of community for myself right here where I'm at.

The importance of having friends and family members in our lives who are supportive and authentic cannot be overstated. This is a vital component of the nourishing Primary Food we need to sustain ourselves through life's hardships and beyond. No one is going to take on the responsibility of creating those meaningful connections for us. If you feel that you're lacking in a sufficient support system, it's time to do something about that. We all need people around us who will lift us up and, when necessary, carry us. I might have walked into some of my weekly home group meetings feeling depleted and even hopeless, but nearly always left feeling loved, empowered and energized. And that is my hope for you as well.

You don't have to commit to a weekly home group to build a support system for yourself. Finding at least one or two like-minded people that you share common ground with is a great place to start. These might be family members, neighbors, old friends, new friends, or possibly people you see at church or school on a regular basis. Online support groups are also an option for people with related challenges or needs, although not an ideal substitute for real life interaction.

It takes time to develop a strong bond that only comes from sharing history with people, but the investment is well worth your time and energy. You can begin today by setting a time to meet up with someone to share in a meaningful, heart-to-heart conversation. It's only in the deep places that we forge the type of bond that truly nourishes and supports us.

• • •

Continue to make room for

community in your life and you'll

soon discover how doing so can help

you cope through whatever difficult

situation you may be facing.

You aren't meant to battle alone.

• • •

Drawing Boundaries

• • •

"You get what you tolerate."

HENRY CLOUD

• • •

When it comes to setting boundaries in a crisis, there is no cut-and-dry guide out there telling us what to do. Learning to set healthy boundaries for myself proved to be one of the most challenging aspects of my journey through trauma and loss. There is so much wrapped up in the matter of boundary setting. My own self-respect was confronted as I found myself frequently in a position of having to go against my loyal-to-a-fault nature, of having to make choices for myself and my family that threatened to shatter my weary heart.

Early on it became evident to me that I would have to be diligent in setting boundaries concerning the voices I allowed into my circumstances. As you may know already, well-meaning people come out of the woodwork in hopes of "helping" you when you enter a crisis. Everyone has an opinion and most really do have the best of intentions, but the multitude of voices can sometimes bring unwelcome confusion. While there were times when I invited input and even relied upon it, I often found myself paralyzed, unable to make a decision as I weighed the many pieces of conflicting advice in my tired head.

Making hard decisions is just one of the demands placed on us when we find ourselves in the midst of life's hardships. Maybe you're walking through a serious illness with a loved one and having to make tough choices regarding treatment. Or perhaps you're experiencing a heartbreaking loss and making your way through the heap of decisions that comes when someone we love is suddenly gone. The most difficult decisions in life do seem to come when we're in the thick of it. My best advice during these times is to draw upon the strength and wisdom of a trusted few (emphasis on the word *few*) and respectfully dismiss the rest. This is not being selfish or rude; this is taking care of yourself and those who genuinely love you will understand.

Believe me, I know how trying it can be to make complicated decisions under stress. I tend to be one who will endure a difficult situation longer than most. It's a part of my personality. Sometimes that looks like steadfastness. And at other times that looks like self-destruction. It's a real challenge to recognize the fine line between the two when our loved ones are involved. Drawing boundaries can be easy enough with the people on the periphery of our lives, the ones who aren't directly affected by what we're going through. But when it comes to the ones we're committed to, such as our spouse and our children, setting boundaries can be both confusing and painful.

There came a point in my journey through Peter's extended season of suffering that I found myself faced with the greatest challenge of my life in regards to boundaries. While there was much I had dealt with in our marriage that many would have considered to be intolerable, I initially chose to stick by my husband because he was unwell and I hoped for his eventual recovery. I had every intention of seeing my husband through to the other side of his torment and planned to be standing right by his side when that day came. Even an unfaithful heart didn't sway me, at least not for a long time. I knew who Peter really was. The man that I married had always demonstrated utmost integrity and absolute faithfulness. Anything less than that came in as a result of his affliction.

But the day did eventually come when too many lines had been crossed, when I felt that my children and I were no longer safe, and I had to ask my husband to leave. I knew in my gut that this was absolutely what I had to do but that didn't make it any easier. After holding on so tightly for so long, letting go felt like I was freefalling into a terrifying and uncertain future. As I watched my husband, the man I still fiercely loved, pack up his vehicle with what looked to be camping essentials and a surfboard, I wanted to beg him to stay. I knew he was vulnerable and potentially in danger. I'd rather live with him knowing that he was safe than live without him.

Following the advice of trusted friends and family as well as legal counsel, I filed for divorce within days of Peter's departure. I did so to protect myself from any liability connected to Peter's actions and also to have the option of finalizing the divorce if it ever came to that. But my heart was always for Peter's healing and the ultimate redemption of our marriage. I believed that filing for divorce was just a part of our future victorious testimony.

But what would I tell the kids? How would I explain this to our extended family? What would other people think? Where would Peter go and who would be there to protect him? And what if he never came back? These questions and more tormented me as I stood in the garage watching him drive away. My heart broke while I simultaneously breathed a sigh of relief. No longer would I assume responsibility for my husband's recovery. No longer would I play the watchdog, standing guard over Peter and watching his every move for warning signs. No longer would I enable him to disrespect me or our marriage covenant, even if his mental state was compromised. It was time to release my husband fully into God's loving care.

Peter didn't give me any clue as to where he was going. As I had learned to do many times before, I tracked his whereabouts by keeping an eye on the bank expenses that cleared our account. I had to fight off the temptation to go after him. Lying in bed wrestling with all of the conflicting emotions that were vying for my heart's attention, I heard a voice come out of nowhere that brought peace to it all. "It's time to lay down your sword and let Me fight for you."

I could do that? Was I really being given permission to stop fighting? To do so felt like giving up more control than I felt comfortable with, and yet I knew that the freedom I longed for was available to me in this decision to fully surrender. I knew that I was not meant to rescue Peter this time, even if it went against every fiber of my faithful being. This was the difficult line I had to draw between myself and my own husband, the one who was such an intimate part of me.

My decision was confirmed when the next Sunday morning message I heard from Pastor Bill Johnson was one in which he talked about the importance of knowing the season we're in. He literally used the exact words God had spoken so gently to me days before. "Know when it's a season to pick up your sword and fight or a season to lay it down and let God fight for you." This illustration became a huge key in my decision-making process from that time on.

Prior to this point, I never really considered the fact that fighting was optional. Now I was being granted permission to step away from the battle. It was time to direct my energies towards some much-needed self-care and the care of my vulnerable young children. It was time to decide what I needed to heal and feel safe while still remaining open to the possibility of a miracle.

Laying down my sword was my way of drawing a healthy boundary for myself, a decision that I didn't take lightly. In fact, walking this decision out was a choice I had to make over and over again in the days and months that followed. Each day was a new day to surrender my sense of responsibility for my husband and for the outcome of our story. For me, *not fighting* was more difficult than fighting for Peter's restoration because it was in the act of fighting that I felt like I was somehow participating in his healing. It turns out that I could also participate by partnering with God's sovereignty and allowing myself to rest in that. His eyes were on Peter even while mine couldn't be.

Following about six months of separation, a sudden breakthrough came and Peter began communicating to me via video calls that he wanted to be home with the kids and me. The clarity in his thinking was surprising and I felt the familiarity of the man I knew and loved returning. After much discussion, prayer and counsel, I welcomed my husband home in September of 2013 and we called off our divorce, finally burning our divorce papers together on our sixteenth anniversary.

Inviting my husband home didn't mean that it was time to stop drawing boundaries. Prior to his homecoming, I made my new boundaries known. I needed to feel safe and cared for. I needed him to pursue complete healing through whatever means necessary. To stop caring for himself was to stop caring for the kids and I. This was not an option for me. I had experienced too much growth and healing to ever go back to the pain and chaos I had lived in before. I would no longer be the enabler, the rescuer, or the caregiver as long as he was capable of caring for himself.

I know that you might feel otherwise, but redemption is actually *not* up to you. If you've been making a martyr out of yourself thinking that the outcome of your situation is solely up to you, relax. It's time to love yourself at least as much as you love the ones involved in your challenging circumstances. Sometimes, as in my own situation, complicated choices are involved in setting boundaries as we make room for God to bring about redemption in His own way. And until that redemption comes, things are not going to get any better for you until you can learn to establish a safe haven for yourself.

Please take some time to consider what you need to practice responsible self-care. You may have people asking you if they can help. If so, take them up on it. If not, let those around you know what you need and, if you're able, hire help where necessary. Have someone clean your house for you every now and then or take over your yard work. You're not a failure if you have someone else step in to assist you in taking care of your children from time to time.

Thriving in the face of adversity requires getting over feeling like a burden and saying yes to enlisting practical support. Remember, this is only for a season. People want to help. Be clear about what you need and keep your boundaries clear for all involved. Don't feel like you have to share openly about your circumstances with everyone who asks. If you haven't already, find a way to communicate what you feel is a reasonable amount of information with the ones you decide to share with. My point here is that *you* get to decide what your boundaries are, who will be part of your inner circle, and who won't.

My hope for you today is that you will feel safe and cared for. Know the season that you are in and what you need to get through it well. Oftentimes we become so engrossed in our circumstances that we can't see where or how to make a change. Perhaps now would be a good time to pull in a close friend or even a professional to help you pinpoint exactly what healthy limits look like for you during this time.

• • •

If you feel sapped of strength or out

of control, the implementation of healthy

boundaries will prove to be restorative

for your body, mind and soul.

• • •

HELPING OTHERS

• • •

"It is one of the beautiful compensations of life that no man can sincerely help another without helping himself."

RALPH WALDO EMERSON

• • •

Among the many ways of stepping outside of our difficult circumstances, helping others is one of my personal favorites. The simple act of demonstrating tender compassion towards another seems to hold a key to unlocking our own sense of joy and wellbeing. I've personally experienced this truth in tangible ways as a health coach. It didn't take long for me to recognize that my decision to support others through their health challenges brought about unexpected fringe benefits in my own life.

As I mentioned earlier, I was smack dab in the middle of a raging storm when I woke up one day and decided to pursue a career in the health and wellness field. At the time, I was spending a large portion of my days in bed unable to fully care for myself, let alone my family. I knew that if my situation was ever going to improve, I had to make a change. I had to take care of me and I wanted to help others in similar situations as well. And that's what I did. Of all the things I chose to do during that season, helping others seemed to bring about the greatest degree of healing in my body, soul and spirit.

I have a confession to make. I honestly can't tell you how many times I went into a health coaching call dressed in my pajamas and an embarrassing amount of dread. "Why did I sign up for this again?" I would ask myself. Here I was feeling miserable and hopeless and thinking that I could somehow offer support to someone else. Had I lost my mind? How could I possibly help someone else when clearly I didn't yet know enough to help my own self?

Well, I went ahead with those coaching calls and, lo and behold, I ended every single session feeling like a champion. My clients became more than faceless strangers who needed what little I felt I had to offer; they became my friends. As they opened up about their own personal challenges and debilitating fears, our hearts connected across the globe and a mutual camaraderie was sparked. I gave all that I had to give at the time and somehow as I poured myself out I was simultaneously filled up. I simply shared with them what I was learning to implement in my own broken life. Surprisingly, that seemed to be enough to help us both.

As I grew in my knowledge and confidence as a health coach, my self-esteem increased. It felt good to know that I had something to offer the world after all. My suffering was absolutely not in vain. By the grace of God I was able to turn the aftermath of my own personal collapse into a platform that allowed me to reach others in need. My personal growth skyrocketed right along with my physical and emotional health. It was nothing short of miraculous. To this day I'm grateful for those early clients who allowed me to be a part of their lives and unknowingly participated in my healing as well as their own.

There's actually a scientific explanation for the mental and emotional benefits I experienced from helping others. We've already learned about the benefits of a runner's high in an earlier chapter. Well, as it turns out there's also such a thing as a helper's high. The same endorphins that are released from physical activity, such as running, are the same endorphins we enjoy when giving of ourselves for the benefit of others. According to Mental Health America, "Research indicates that those who consistently help other people experience less depression, greater calm, fewer pains and better health. They may even live longer."[1]

This perfectly describes the boost I felt (and continue to feel) while practicing as a health coach. I've also experienced a similar phenomenon when taking a meal to a friend, donating resources to a cause I believe in, or offering food and clothing to a homeless person. I walk away feeling uplifted simply by knowing that I was able to make the life of someone else a little better.

If you want to become a healthier, happier, more fulfilled version of yourself then here's your opportunity. I've put together a list of ideas for helping others in a variety of ways. This is just a start, but I believe that there is *something* in this list that any one of us could do. As you peruse this list, pencil in a star next to anything that you know you're able to do either today or in the near future.

- Assist in a soup kitchen

- Sponsor a child

- Visit the elderly in a retirement or convalescent home

- Take a meal to a new mom

- Smile at a stranger

- Become a mentor in your community

- Support a missionary family

- Contribute to an adoption fund for someone you know

- Secretly pick up the tab for a stranger at a restaurant

- Coach a sports team

- Volunteer at a charity

- Stop to help a person in need

- Send a note of appreciation to someone

- Donate food or clothing to a homeless shelter

- Redirect your birthday gifts to your favorite charity

- Offer a free date night out to parents of young children

- Become a CASA (court appointed social advocate)

- Give someone a meaningful hug

- Volunteer to work with children at a school or church

- Teach someone else a skill you've mastered

It's sometimes difficult to feel like you could be helpful to anyone at all when you're feeling down. You might be feeling lonely, depressed, hopeless or even physically ill. If this is the case, I urge you to choose one simple act of kindness from the list I've provided and do it anyway. It could be something as simple as smiling at a stranger or holding a door open for someone. You don't have to wait for your circumstances to improve to help others.

• • •

Giving of yourself connects you

to others, takes your mind off of your

own troubles and reduces stress. Find a

way to help others today and, before

you know it, that helper's high will be

kicking in and you'll be enjoying a much-

needed boost in health and happiness.

• • •

Prioritizing You

...

"When you recover or discover something that nourishes your soul and brings joy, care enough about yourself to make room for it in your life."

JEAN SHINODA BOLEN

...

Why is it that we can be so quick to show respect, value, and compassion to others while struggling deeply with extending an equal measure of grace to the person looking back at us in the mirror? Why is it that we tend to pour all that we have to give out for those around us while neglecting ourselves? And why is it that we feel so horribly guilty when we do finally take the time to nurture our own needs, desires, and dreams? This has got to stop.

An article in *Psychology Today* addresses this topic well:

> *"Our failure to stop and check in with ourselves and make time for the things that are meaningful to us can increase our stress. Filling our lives with responsibilities can generate a cycle in which being stressed feels like the norm. As a society, we are unapologetic about our stress levels, even wearing them like a badge of honor, proving our value. However, stress takes a serious toll on our mental and physical health. These effects often catch up with us and prevent us from enjoying our lives, not to mention affecting how we relate to others, often leading to more conflict, tension, and acting out in our relationships."* [1]

Even with the facts before us, I do understand how extra challenging it can be to prioritize yourself when either you or the people around you are hurting. Focusing on our own needs feels horribly selfish in light of the pain and heartache that's staring us in the face. But please hear me. If there was ever a time to make yourself a priority, it's now. Loving yourself well is a vital part of getting through hardships with your hope and health in tact. Just ask me how I know.

I've been the martyr, the one denying myself of what I needed most thinking I was doing something great. I've been the one to compromise my common sense and personal boundaries while enabling someone else's brokenness to continue unnecessarily. And I've been the one to work so tirelessly at fixing problems that weren't my own that I forgot how to take care of myself. A lifestyle such as this can dangerously approach the brink of codependency if you're not cautious. It wasn't until my own health was in jeopardy that I learned the true value of prioritizing myself. Today I want to suggest to you some ways to do that very thing.

But before I get into that, I have a question for you. When you hear the voice coming from inside your own head, is it kind and respectful? Is it the voice of a true friend? If not, then it's time to do something about that. Valuing and loving yourself is the first step in prioritizing you.

Coming from a place of battling a low self-esteem for most of my life, I know how critical, demeaning and downright stubborn those derogatory voices in our heads can be. Sometimes, those internal voices are merely the echoes of others in our past who have carelessly put us down. At times, the lies we have unknowingly come to believe about ourselves speak more loudly than the truth. It's in our best interests to identify those voices, call them out for what they are and love ourselves enough to replace them with truth.

It's time to start talking to yourself like you would someone you deeply care about. Fellow health coach MaryAnn Jones of Thrive Naturally recommends thinking about how you would like to feel and embracing language that supports your goals. A suitable mantra might be, "I am important and take steps to thrive every day."[2] A positive statement such as this one can serve as an excellent tool for imprinting truth upon our hearts and minds.

You may recall that unforgettable line from the movie *The Help*, "You is smart. You is kind. You is important." Peter and I said that to one another and our children for weeks after seeing the film. I even caught him saying it to himself in the mirror one day and we both had a good laugh. Whatever it is you need to be reminded of most, write it down and post it on your bathroom mirror. Say it out loud. Say it until you believe it more than the lying voices in your head.

Now I want you to ask yourself another question. When did you last take time out for you? Can you remember? If it's been a while, I want you to set aside a little time today to tune into your own needs. Have you felt depleted, low on steam and a bit edgy with those around you lately? If so, then odds are it's time to give yourself a well-deserved break. The only question left to answer is, what would you like to do?

Even if it's only ten to fifteen minutes in the morning before you do anything else, decide on an activity that you enjoy. The only rule is, you can't feel guilty for doing it! Here are some ideas:

- Read something just for fun

- Do some relaxation stretches

- Take a bubble bath

- Give yourself a facial

- Write in a journal

- Step outside for a brisk walk

- Relax in your cozy clothes with a hot drink

- Worship, pray and/or meditate

- Call an encouraging friend or family member

I'm sure you could expand upon this list of simple self-care activities with other ways to treat yourself. This is something that I want you to build upon in your own unique way. Maybe you can soon carve out an hour here or there for some pampering time or physical activity that feeds your soul. As you begin to add these happy moments to your day, I believe you'll begin to notice how much more relaxed and satisfied you feel. And when you feel better, you're in a more healthy position to serve others in your world. As author and filmmaker Stephen Chbosky states, "You can't just sit there and put everyone's lives ahead of yours and think that counts as love. You just can't."

Taking care of yourself is not a selfish luxury. If you want to truly thrive in life, it's as essential as the air you breathe. Neglecting yourself makes no more sense than driving your car for months and years without ever getting a tune-up. Your car would soon cease to function properly and so would you. So starting today, let's kick guilt to the curb and extend full permission to be as kind and loving to ourselves as we are to our dearest, most treasured friends.

• • •

Thriving begins with you taking the best possible care of you.

• • •

BREATHING DEEPLY

• • •

*"People who eat excellent diets and exercise faithfully
are not always healthy, but the likelihood of being a healthy
person who does not breathe well is slim."*

DR. ANDREW WEIL

• • •

While we've already discussed lots of ways to combat stress, we can't
overlook the powerful stress buster that literally exists right under our
noses. The practice of intentional deep breathing is another amaz-
ingly potent God-given tool available to us anytime, anywhere. Even
young children possess the ability to train their physical responses to
stressful situations through deep breathing exercises. While this might
sound elementary, today I want to explain to you why proper breathing techniques are so effective and how to get the most out of your
own deep breathing routine.

I was preparing for the birth of my first baby back in 2003 when I discovered how harnessing the power of breathing and relaxation can transform an event so intense and stressful as childbirth into a peaceful, nearly painless process. Developed by Dr. Robert A. Bradley, the appropriately named Bradley Method of natural childbirth has been around since 1947, teaching couples to manage labor through deep breathing. It was this husband-coached method that empowered me to take charge of my own birth experience in such a way that I was able to enter into this foreign-to-me experience without fear.

My doula encouraged me to practice relaxation and deep breathing for months in advance. I would do so by getting comfortable on my side, snuggling up with a large body pillow. I would then quiet my mind and tune into every bit of tension in my body. Starting at the top of my head, I slowly relaxed every part of my oversized self all the way down to my swollen toes. I breathed deep into my belly with each intentional release of stress. The resulting effect was powerful enough to put me nearly to sleep, which is saying a lot for this sleep-challenged soul.

When delivery day came two weeks prior to my anticipated due date, I first of all thanked God for His well-timed mercy and, second of all, spent the first few hours of my labor session in our pool. Since Peter wasn't expecting me to give birth so soon, he wasn't quite ready to leave his work as administrator of the home for boys where we lived and served. I watched him rush around from house to house on the property trying to get things in order while I floated limply in the water, practicing the breathing exercises that had now become a habit. When the contractions became particularly intense, I would call out to him across the property, "Peter! Please hurry!!!" (It's only funny now.)

Quincy, my sweet doula, arrived and decided that we should go ahead and make the thirty-minute trek across the valley to the hospital in Palm Springs. Once I got through the uncomfortable drive and settled into my room, my birth plan went into effect. While the lights were dimmed and my choice of music was turned on, I went into my familiar zone of relaxation. Despite the relentless nausea and back labor, I was able to remain in a peaceful, relaxed state for the majority of the lengthy delivery. With each set of contractions I went inward, breathing as deeply into my belly as I possibly could and breathing slowly out while silently repeating my mental mantra, "In with the peace, out with the pain…" over and over and over again.

Before my eight-and-half-pound Alex would enter the world with a little help from a suction device and one hurried obstetrician, nearly every person who entered the delivery room remarked on the unusually peaceful atmosphere enveloping us. While Alex's delivery would turn out to be by far the longest of all my children, I'll always remember it as my most calm and enjoyable childbirth experience. All of the time that I had invested in preparing for the birth of our son paid off with the drug-free delivery that I had hoped for. I can tell you now that there is *no way* I would have been able to do that if not for the deep breathing techniques I employed along the way.

The same powerful effects of deep breathing are available to you. You might not be preparing to give birth, but if your innate stress response is chronically activated, you can benefit greatly from using intentional relaxation techniques. Unfortunately, if we neglect to protect ourselves against the damaging effects of a hyper-alert sympathetic nervous system, we will soon suffer from impaired immune response, increased anxiety, and depression among other things. This is not exactly going to lead us towards the thriving life we desire.

When you breathe deeply into the lower lobes of your lungs, you send a message to your brain telling it to relax. The longer you practice this, the more you'll enjoy the benefits of doing so with a lower heart rate, reduced tension, improved digestion, lower blood pressure, and less physical pain (yes, even in childbirth). The production of the harmful stress hormones we've previously discussed is greatly diminished as the sympathetic nervous system, otherwise known as the "fight or flight" mechanism, is given permission to chill out. In turn, we're able to enter into the "rest and digest" mode thanks to the activation of the parasympathetic nervous system.

According to the American Institute of Stress, abdominal breathing for twenty to thirty minutes each day will reduce anxiety and stress levels significantly.[1] The increased oxygen level in the brain is responsible for the sense of calm associated with the parasympathetic nervous system. Intentional breathing techniques cause us to feel more connected to our bodies as we turn our attention away from our worries and, instead, enjoy a calm and quiet mind. And who doesn't need a little more of that these days?

When I was going through a particularly stressful time a few years ago, a chiropractor had me lay on my back and breathe deeply. As I followed her instructions, my chest raised and lowered with each slow breath. Then she asked me to place my hand on top of my belly and try again, only this time breathing in such a way that I moved my hand instead of my upper chest. Quickly realizing how out of practice I had become in my deep breathing routine, I felt a little like I was clumsily attempting to pat my belly and rub my head at the same time. But with the patient coaching of the chiropractor, I was finally able to keep my chest steady while my belly contracted and expanded through the exercise.

Now why do you think she had me do this? Wasn't I there for a spinal adjustment, not a lesson in breathing? Well, this doctor knew that if I was going to experience any relief from my chronic stress and resulting muscle tension, I was going to have to find a way to activate my parasympathetic nervous system. While I had little control over the sources of my stress at the time, I did have the ability to counteract the stress just as I did through the intense birth of my son. This was possible thanks to the calming and repairing nerve receptors that exist in the lower lobes of the lungs (as opposed to the fight or flight stress receptors found in the upper lobes). It's important to note that deep breathing through the nose, rather than the mouth, drives even more oxygen into the lower lobes.[2]

Any Google search on this topic will yield at least a dozen different ways to go about establishing a deep breathing practice. You're welcome to adopt whatever works best for you. For our purposes in this chapter, I'm going to teach you one simple voluntary regulated breathing practice (or VRBP). You can do this absolutely anywhere, anytime, but ideally I'd suggest that you pick a regular time and place to practice deep breathing.

- Get as relaxed and comfortable as possible.

- Close your eyes.

- Inhale slowly through the nose, into the belly for a count of four.

- Hold for two counts.

- Exhale slowly through the mouth for at least four counts, forcing as much air out of the lungs as possible. (This allows more room for oxygen during your next inhale.)

- Pause for two counts.

- Repeat for as long as you desire.

I do want to mention one word of caution on this topic. I'm not one to suffer from anxiety attacks, but I did endure two memorable bouts of hyperventilation following the loss of my husband. I remember how scary that was and how legitimately impossible it felt to catch my breath. I couldn't have practiced deep breathing if I wanted to, and I did try. In a case such as this, deep breathing is *not* recommended for someone who is experiencing a panic attack, shortness of breath, or hyperventilation for any reason.

I learned of this exception recently while attending a seminar by the Institute for Brain Potential on the habits of stress-resilient people.[3] I had been wrongly suggesting to a family member with an anxiety disorder that she should take slow, deep breaths while trying to ward off a panic attack. I honestly thought that I was helping her activate her parasympathetic nervous system, but instead I was only adding more oxygen to her already overly-oxygenated blood, making it nearly impossible to restore normal breathing.

Without getting into the detailed physiology behind why, I'll just say that a better option under such circumstances would be deeply breathing into a paper bag for about one minute. This has something to do with re-breathing the carbon dioxide stored in the bag back into the lungs, consequently restoring the body's pH to normal levels along with a normal breathing pattern. Normal breathing may return in as little as twenty seconds, but it's best to continue for closer to one full minute. Apparently breathing into a paper bag is more than just an old wives tale!

To establish this new deep breathing routine, I recommend that you set a goal of practicing this technique once or twice a day for between ten and twenty minutes. I hope that this powerful relaxation tool not only benefits you by reducing your stress levels, but becomes a habit that you look forward to and enjoy on a daily basis.

• • •

The practice of deep breathing

on a regular basis can be

enough to boost not only your

immune system, but your

entire outlook on life.

• • •

Connecting with Nature

• • •

"Resilient people stop to smell the roses."

JOHN D. PRESTON, PSY.D.

• • •

Returning home from an out-of-town summer adventure with four of our children on my own, I promptly dropped them off at the house and immediately headed for the nearby walking trails. Not really knowing which direction I would take or how long I would walk for, I only knew that I needed to be alone and I needed to be in nature. Normally our kids are fairly easy travelers, but this nearly four hundred-mile journey home with them had pushed me to my wit's end. The bickering, whining, and complaining had exhausted me. My frayed nerves desperately needed some down time before re-entering my high-demand life back at home.

Walking until I found a shaded bench overlooking a lake, I planted myself in that scenic space for over an hour. Tears of frustration and weariness washed over my cheeks while my eyes soaked in the tranquilizing beauty of creation all around me. The stillness, the way the beams of sunlight danced across the water, the squawking geese flying overhead, and the squirrels chasing each other around the tree next to me—all of it ministered deeply to my tired soul.

After a long period of solitude, my husband called and allowed me to process my mess of emotions with him. I often joke that Lance missed his calling as a counselor. He truly knows how to listen and respond in such a way that leaves me feeling known, loved, and secure. (This may or may not have been a huge factor in my falling in love with him.) Giving me all the time and space that I needed, he welcomed me home for dinner when I was ready. I soaked in every last drop of nature's healing power. I don't know about you, but there's no place else that I feel closer to God than I do when I'm surrounded by His creation.

My friend Rachel recently described to me how time spent connecting with nature has played a role in her healing process after the sudden loss of her husband, Stewart, in a tragic water skiing accident.

I always loved backpacking with my husband. When he died I decided it was important for me to recover and hold onto the things that were so special to me. I gathered friends and family to go backpacking on behalf of my husband and was able to make some really special memories that way. I found that nature was very soothing to my soul. I would lay in the grass under the trees and listen to the wind, journaling my thoughts and prayers while contemplating the deep things in life.

Like Rachel, whose inspiring story you can read at the end of this book, I have also felt an insatiable craving to be outdoors in the midst of heartache—and for good reason. A 2013 article in National Geographic explains a biological correlation between time spent in nature and happiness. "As nature-connectedness increases, so does mood, cognition, vitality, and life satisfaction. Many of these effects are caused by contact with certain bacterias not found in city settings. Some of these bacteria are known for fighting illnesses like chronic fatigue syndrome, anxiety, and depression."[1]

In an electronic world where we struggle against the increasing pull towards screen-time addiction, the more we desperately need adequate time connecting with nature to balance the scales. Richard Louv, author of the bestsellers *Last Child in the Woods* (2005) and *The Nature Principle* (2011), coined the term "nature-deficit disorder" to describe this loss of connection with the natural world. Lance and I notice the effects of diminished play time in nature on our own children compared to the way we both grew up freely exploring the natural areas near our childhood homes.

As our evolving American lifestyle continually brings us more indoors than ever, we miss out on the many benefits of natural healing through modalities such as grounding, also known as earthing. While some might be tempted to dismiss the validity of the claims made about earthing as mere hippie lore, science continues to prove that earthing provides electric nutrition generated by the earth itself. How amazing it is that this powerful healing source is always available to us and always free! All we have to do is choose to take advantage of it.

In one study published in 2015, the positive effects of grounding on the body were documented with medical infrared imaging.[2] Besides the notable effects of grounding on sleep, the abundant source of mobile electrons on the surface of the earth were shown to provide for us the very best source of antioxidants available. These antioxidants serve to rapidly reduce inflammation throughout the body. And, as you may know, chronic inflammation is the root cause of many diseases.

Benefits of grounding include reduced pain, stress and tension as well as a stronger immune system. There is also something to be said for the earth's ability to counteract the harmful effects inflicted upon us by our constant exposure to electronic devices. If you're feeling under the weather, in pain, or just plain stressed out, give grounding a try while you participate in your favorite outdoor activity.

Whether it's sitting on the beach, gardening, reading, camping, or picnicking, kick off your shoes and connect the soles of your feet to the earth. Soil, grass, sand, and concrete are all conductive surfaces that allow us to draw on the earth's electrical healing energy. Aim for spending a minimum of thirty minutes each day connecting your body with the surface of the earth. Combine this with your choice of other stress-relieving tools we've covered and you'll reap exponential rewards!

If you can't get outside and savor some time in nature today, I encourage you to look at your calendar and carve out a space to do so in the near future. As with any new healthy habit, it's the consistent practice that will provide you with the results you're looking for.

...

Try practicing your deep

breathing exercises while

grounding in nature and

stress doesn't stand a chance.

...

Applying Aromatherapy

• • •

"Aromatherapy is a caring, hands-on therapy which seeks to induce relaxation, to increase energy, to reduce the effects of stress and to restore lost balance to mind, body and soul."

ROBERT TISSERAND, AUTHOR OF *THE ART OF AROMATHERAPY*

• • •

Essential oils are commonly used for immune support, stress relief, relaxation, skin care, respiratory health, sleep enhancement, muscle tension and pain reduction, mood support and emotional balance. Today I'll guide you in some simple ways to incorporate the healing power of aromatherapy into your life as well as some basic education in regards to usage and safety. But first, I want to give you a little of my background on this subject.

It was about twenty years ago when I first discovered the seemingly endless therapeutic uses of essential oils. As a young newlywed, I was excited about the idea of using aromatherapy for anything from fighting off sickness to safely and effectively cleaning our home with my homemade products. Tea tree oil, also known as melaleuca, was the first oil I ever tried and it remains my personal favorite to this day. With the explosion of a couple of major essential oil companies in recent years, it's now more common than ever to hear someone say, "I've got an oil for that."

While I was certainly glad to see a rise in awareness surrounding this ancient healing modality, I was also concerned by the irresponsible usage I witnessed at times. Suddenly it seemed as though everyone thought of themselves as an aromatherapist. I saw people ingesting oils, applying them to their babies and pets and also applying oils directly to the skin that could be harmful. There are ways to do all of these things safely, but without adequate education or support from a qualified practitioner, it's important to exercise caution.

Because I wanted to know how to best advise my clients on the safe and proper use of these popular botanicals, I decided to pursue my certification as an aromatherapist in 2013. One of my major concerns with the widespread use of essential oils these days is the way people are using them internally. The majority of oils are not safe for undiluted use on our external skin, let alone our delicate internal skin.

I realize that ingesting oils has become commonplace for some, but you won't find me recommending it. For one, it can be potentially damaging to our mucous membranes and gut lining and, two, it's simply not necessary. Both inhalation and skin application are sufficiently effective methods for infusing the therapeutic compounds available in the oils into the bloodstream quickly.

INHALATION

Inhaling essential oils provides a quick way to deliver many therapeutic benefits to the whole body through the bloodstream. Olfac-
tion, otherwise known as smelling, sends messages from the nose to
the brain nearly instantaneously. Tiny molecules contained in essential oils stimulate the olfactory system which communicates directly
with the central nervous system, providing us with a powerful tool for
calming ourselves down when necessary. I personally find the science
behind this fascinating!

Scent has a way of reaching our subconscious mind unlike any of
our other senses. You've probably noticed how quickly a certain smell
can so quickly affect your mood. This is thanks to the limbic system,
the parts of the brain that are responsible for establishing emotional
states. When the smell of fresh baked chocolate chip cookies instantly
takes you back to your childhood, you've just experienced an example of how the limbic system evokes long-term memories and their
related emotional responses.

TOPICAL APPLICATION

Applying oils to the skin not only affects the skin directly, but also provides another highly effective vehicle for introducing essential oils into
the bloodstream. It's always safe to assume that anything applied to
the skin can cross into the deeper tissues and into the bloodstream,
which is why it's wise to pay close attention to the ingredients in our
cosmetics and any skin care products we use. Areas with thin skin, lots
of hair, and mucous membranes (internal skin) absorb more quickly.
While the soles of our feet have an extra layer of skin, they also contain larger pores which allow the increased absorption of essential oils.

If you've been using essential oils for a while, you may have heard the term "neat." In the realm of aromatherapy, "neat" refers to the undiluted application of essential oils. While some oils are safe for neat application, others must be diluted with a safe carrier oil such as fractionated coconut oil or jojoba wax, for example. Some oils can cause irritation or chemical burns while others are phototoxic, meaning that they can damage the skin when introduced to UV light.

There are essential oils that are actually nourishing and healing when applied in full concentration to the skin, but even these should still be used in small amounts for short periods of time. Some commonly used essential oils that fit this description are lavender, tea tree, and frankincense oils. I've personally used all of these oils for successfully healing anything from minor scrapes and burns to suspicious pre-cancerous spots on my face.

AROMATHERAPY BY PLANT PART

When it comes to choosing an essential oil or a blend of oils for a specific purpose, the list of options can feel overwhelming. To help you narrow down your choices, I want you to think about essential oils in terms of the part of the plant they are extracted from. It's important to tune in to the mental or emotional effect you are looking for prior to selecting an oil. Once you know that, you can consider what part of the plant might offer that therapeutic benefit. I'll break this down further for you by a listing a handful of the main plant parts along with some of my favorite essential oils (although I can't possibly list them all) and their therapeutic properties.

Flowers: Oils extracted from flowers fill the air with their floral, sweet aromas. They are uplifting and provide excellent emotional support. They soothe the heart and the mind. Some examples are chamomile, jasmine, lavender, rose and ylang ylang.

Fruit: Fruit oils are a favorite in our family, offering refreshing scents that everyone can enjoy. These oils are cleansing, refreshing, uplifting, and possess the therapeutic ability to lift depression and encourage creativity. Try juniper berry or any citrus oil such as lemon, lime, orange, grapefruit or bergamot.

Leaves: Leaf oils help us breathe more efficiently. When we feel the constricting effects of stress or anxiety, these oils can help reduce racing thoughts, bringing us back into a calm, clear mind. A few of my favorites are eucalyptus, helichrysum, laurel leaf, peppermint and tea tree.

Roots: Oils derived from roots are anchoring, grounding, and settling. Root oils offer a sense of stability and balance. These are great for someone feeling anxious and disconnected. Examples of root oils are fingerroot (similar to ginger) and vetiver, an oil that I highly recommend for the treatment of insomnia.

CALMING BLENDS

I want to provide you with a couple of blends for emotional balancing that you can make at home. Both of these blends not only smell wonderful, but are also specifically formulated for the purpose of calming the central nervous system and lifting mood.

BALANCING CREAM

3 drops of Neroli

3 drops of Sweet Orange

1 drop of Frankincense

1 drop of Lemon

1 drop of Ylang Ylang

Stir into 1 ounce of unscented
lotion and apply as desired.

ANTI-ANXIETY INHALER

1 drop of Ylang Ylang

8 drops of Bergamot Mint

3 drops of Lavender

2 drops of Roman Chamomile

Add oils to a blank cotton inhaler.
(available for purchase at aromatics.com)

Use inhaler whenever anxiety
symptoms present themselves.

FOR BEGINNERS

If you are new to practicing aromatherapy, you can get started with only one or two essential oils. My initial suggestions would be tea tree and lavender oils. You can use both of them safely in undiluted form on your skin without worry. You can also add a couple of drops to your bath or shower or even your shampoo. If you have a diffuser, you can add a few drops of each and enjoy the benefits for hours.

Speaking of diffusers, I have tried quite a few and I have one for every room in the house. The one brand that has never failed me is MIU and you can find them at *amazon.com*. They're now more affordable than ever and available in color-changing styles or faux wood finishes. I've had mine for many years and never had a problem with one yet.

As you begin to build your own essential oil collection, please make sure that you are using one hundred percent pure, responsibly sourced essential oils from a reputable company. Personally, my most trusted source of essential oils and aromatherapy supplies is a company called Aromatics International.[1] I did a lot of research before I chose to order my entire aromatherapy lab four years ago and this is the company that hit all the marks for me.

Wherever you order your oils from, first confirm that the company can provide you with what's called a GC/MS report (short for gas chromatography/mass spectrometry). A GC/MS report tells us which chemical components are found in a specific batch of oil and when it will surpass its unique shelf life. Without this information, there is no way to guarantee that the product is pure or therapeutic grade. If a company can't provide that, they don't have my business.

If aromatherapy is a topic that interests you, you'll probably enjoy getting lost in the incredible amount of information and recipes available at aromatics.com. I promise you that I don't have any affiliation with this company outside of being a customer for several years. I simply believe in their products, services, and philosophy and trust that you'll benefit from them, too.

If you don't have any essential oils available to you at this point, try connecting with a friend who might be willing to share their oils while trying out one of the blend recipes with you. We really only scratched the surface of aromatherapy here, so I hope that you'll dig into this further and soon be enjoying the therapeutic effects of this natural healing practice.

• • •

You can support and enhance

your well being as well as delight

your senses by making essential

oils an everyday part of your life.

• • •

DRESSING UP

...

*"No matter how you feel, get up, dress up,
show up and never give up."*

AUTHOR UNKNOWN

...

Lance and I are blessed with two creative little girls, Alyma and Raine, who are currently ages eight and ten respectively. They are the youngest of our combined seven children. Despite their differing personality types, these two girls melt my heart regularly with their sweet sisterly connection. Their innocent, imaginative play seems to capture the essence of childhood in such a way that I often wish I could freeze them in time and keep them little forever.

One of the girls' favorite things to do together is play dress-up. On any given day we can expect to witness multiple costume changes to match whatever characters they are role playing. Watching them together reminds me so much of my own childhood. My aunt Julie and I are only seven months apart and spent countless hours dressing up in my grandmother's silky nightgowns and long, sparkly necklaces pretending to be living lives of the rich and famous.

Later as a young adult entering the workforce, I found myself learning to dress for success. I spent my first three years out of high school working full-time at City Hall in Redding and I wanted to be taken seriously as the only teenager on staff. When I later moved to southern California in 1995, I held a position assisting about seventy commercial real estate brokers in Newport Beach. You'd better believe I wanted to look the part of a young professional woman in the big city. My part-time job at a popular clothing store helped me accomplish my fashion goals, even if it cost me more than I ever made at that job. But how I dressed really did affect my confidence level in the workplace.

Let's face it. When we look great, we feel great! The feeling can give us such a boost that it can become addicting, as I soon realized in my early working years. But I'm not here to confess my past spending habits to you right now. I merely want to point out that dressing for success is a real thing! It works. When we look successful, we feel successful. People take us seriously. Our confidence soars. And, sooner or later, we *become* successful!

The flipside is also true. When we look like a mess, we feel like a mess. And don't I know this all too well. We've probably all experienced those times when our frumpy mood and matching style has been transformed by a shower and wardrobe change. Have you ever taken note of how much better you feel when you catch a glimpse of yourself in the mirror after getting cleaned up?

Dressing up provides an instant pick-me-up, boosting confidence and mood alike. It's for this reason that I have included dressing up in my self-care toolbox. We aren't going to successfully navigate life's hardships well while we're sulking around in our pajamas. There's a time and a place for cozy clothes and resting days, but let's not get stuck there now, okay?

Times of prolonged stress can often leave us feeling uninspired, sapped of creative energy, and lacking in the desire to spend any effort at all on our appearance. I'm going to suggest that this is precisely the *perfect* opportunity to do exactly the opposite of what you feel! If you look in the mirror and look a little (or a lot) like you've given up, then you probably have. It's high time to trade in that dowdy style for a mood-boosting makeover.

Remember, what you're going through right now is not who you are. Our trials may feel all consuming at times, but they do not define us. Who were you before loss or trauma robbed you of your self-respect? If you've forgotten who you truly are, ask those closest to you for some feedback. I'm willing to bet that your friends and family members will be able to remind you that you're a rockstar in more ways than you realize. So why not look like one?

If you've fallen into the habit of spending your days in the dumps, I want to challenge you to do something about that today. Your appearance doesn't have to match the reality of your life. Haven't you ever heard the saying, "Fake it 'til you make it"? Well I'm not ashamed to say that I've done this very thing to launch myself past my fears and through my inhibitions on multiple occasions.

Take, for example, the first time I spoke at a conference almost five years ago. When I received the initial invitation, my understanding was that I'd be leading an off-stage workshop at a wellness conference. I imagined that the audience would be small, familiar, and unintimidating. However, up to this point I'd spent my entire life paralyzed by the very thought of public speaking in any form. I saw this small workshop as an opportunity to overcome my fear-induced paralysis.

As the event drew closer, the details changed just a tad. This "small workshop" morphed into me being listed as one of the main session speakers at a globally broadcasted conference alongside my own naturopathic physician, Dr. Ronda Nelson. I knew that this growth opportunity was a gift and I'd be a fool to turn it down. But could this situation possibly be any more intimidating?

It was March of 2013 and I'd been in the throes of overcoming my own personal health crash alongside my husband's mental breakdown for about two and a half years. I was several months into becoming a certified health coach at this point, but my experience and education didn't come anywhere *close* to what Dr. Ronda had to offer. There was no getting out of this, so I charged ahead in all-out "fake it 'til you make it" style.

I went shopping. I got my hair done. I prepared the best PowerPoint presentation I knew how. I went on walks during which I pretended to be speaking to my audience. I even practiced in the mirror until finally the big day came. My old fears and insecurities could no longer serve me well. It was time to put on a new me.

So, I dressed the part to the best of my ability and went through the motions as if I was an actress playing the role of someone other than myself. And guess what? I wasn't nervous at all. In fact, I enjoyed myself. This was fun! While I might have thought I was faking it in the beginning, I actually felt like I stepped into the most authentic version of myself I'd ever experienced. This is who I genuinely was when fear and low self-esteem were silenced in my life.

Empowered by this entire process, I went on to say "yes" to other exciting public speaking engagements in the future. One such opportunity landed just four months after the passing of my husband in 2014. I was set to speak at a health summit in Vacaville, California but I didn't really feel like doing it. I had made the commitment in hopes that I would feel stronger when the time came. Grief and stress took a greater toll on me than I had anticipated and I soon wished for a way out of this conference. I just wasn't in the mood.

But, I did go ahead with the plan. I again dressed up and presented myself as the confident "expert" the audience was anticipating. Well, once on stage I knew that my best and only option was to be the real me. After all, the real me was an overcomer. The real me faced my fears and said "yes" in spite of them. And the real me broke down crying right there on stage at the first mention of my late husband.

I remember hearing another session speaker, Beni Johnson, cheer me on from our table off to the right, encouraging me to keep going from the sidelines. Drawing on Beni's encouragement and summoning a strength that was greater than myself, I managed to pull it together and finish my session out well. Once again, I enjoyed it! Now I look back on that day as one of the most victorious experiences of my life. Maybe I had to fake it a little to get myself up there, but doing so was enough to boost my confidence to a level that I was able to master my fear and step into my true identity.

Perhaps you aren't anticipating any public speaking engagements in the near future, but that doesn't mean you can't rise to the challenge. Perhaps this is your moment to step out of the slump you may be in and into a life you never dreamed possible. You don't have to be through the storm you're in now to do this. Today is the perfect day for breaking out of depression, hopelessness, fear, or whatever restricting mindset could be holding you back. Dressing up is just one way to make that happen.

If you need a little motivation to make a change, try planning a lunch date with a friend or scheduling a nice dinner out with your spouse or significant other. Be intentional about what you're going to wear. Give yourself a reason to dress up if that's what you need right now. In time, it's my hope that simply valuing yourself will be reason enough to get up in the morning and dress to express the real you. After all, I see no good reason why dressing up should be reserved only for our children.

• • •

Giving up on yourself

is not an option. It's time

to get up, dress up, and

show up to your life today!

• • •

GETTING ACTIVE

• • •

*"Movement is a medicine for creating change in a person's
physical, emotional, and mental states."*

CAROL WELCH

• • •

How would you like to make one change that would support you in
reducing stress, giving your immune system a boost, improving your
sleep quality, balancing hormones, minimizing anxiety and depression while also losing weight? You're likely already aware that physical activity provides us with all of these amazing benefits and more.
And you don't have to become an elite athlete or a gym enthusiast to
reap the rewards of getting active.

It was an unlikely acquaintance turned supportive friend who first
introduced me to processing my stress through exercise. Although
I had known him since the sixth grade, Joby came back into my life

sometime in the fall of 2012. We shared a mutual friend who told him about my journey with Peter and, as a result, Joby wanted to connect with us. We arranged a lunch meeting during which I mostly sat and listened while Peter and Joby exchanged stories and began building a mutually supportive friendship.

Soon after, I found Peter and Joby engrossed in a project in our backyard building an extraordinary multi-level tree fort for our kids complete with an impressive zip line and fireman's pole. This had been Peter's dream since we purchased our home. Now, with Joby's handy architectural skills, the two of them were able to make it a reality. It was a beautiful thing watching as they worked together side-by-side each day. They seemed to be healing each other somehow.

Unfortunately, Peter's short-lived victory over mental illness began to slip away before my eyes just a few months later. I remember Joby pulling me aside and letting me know that he could see what was happening. It wasn't just my imagination. He expressed his concern and felt I should prepare for the worst. Joby encouraged me to stop working so hard to take care of Peter and, instead, to shift my energies towards taking better care of myself.

Well, Joby's foresight proved to be correct as it wasn't long before Peter regressed into such a severe manic cycle that it became impossible to live together in the same space for a while. I was beside myself, completely overwhelmed by the needs of my young children and the loss of my husband's presence in our home. It didn't matter that he wasn't quite himself, I still missed him terribly.

My heart was broken and my stress was through the roof. Joby continued to come by the house to lend a hand, sometimes taking the kids in the backyard for a trampoline session or a walk to the creek to give me a break. He helped me in many ways but, looking back, the best advice I received from him was through his encouragement to take my stress to the gym. In fact, he even offered to buy me a gym membership.

Joby soon moved out of town, but I kept up with my new gym habit. I was hooked. The relief I experienced in my stress level was enough to keep me going back day after day. Sometimes as I sweated it out on the elliptical trainer with my worship music playing in my ears, I would weep. Thankfully my gym had a women's only area that was usually pretty quiet, so I had a safe place to work out my big emotions free from any curious onlookers. I didn't always feel like I had the energy to go to the gym, but each time I chose to go anyway I reaped the benefits.

During that painful and lonely time of separation from Peter, I became the most fit and healthy version of myself I'd ever known. The more my heart hurt, the harder I pushed in the gym. Before I knew it, I'd lost a whopping twenty-five pounds! I uncovered fresh energy and was now able to keep up with my kids in ways I never dreamed possible. I felt stronger and better about my appearance than I had in my whole adult life. While this wasn't my goal when I began going to the gym, the surprising rewards kept me from sinking as low as I imagine I would have had I not become so physically active.

When Peter returned to our family six months later, I was a better person. I'd launched my business as a health coach, gained a little bit of attention as a newbie conference speaker, learned how to navigate life independently as a single working parent, and dropped four dress sizes. I now looked and felt like the healthy overcomer I had become. It's truly amazing what we can accomplish when we set our minds to it. Had it not been for the challenges I'd faced, I never would have pushed myself past my comfortable limitations.

I don't need to tell you all the ways that exercise will do your body good. For me, the fitness component is a wonderful perk. But more than that, the shift that occurs in my mind when I'm physically active is what truly motivates me to move even when I don't feel like it at first. Every single time that I chose to pull myself out of a depressed slump and into the gym or onto the walking trails, I completed my workout feeling like a free woman. Worrisome distractions no longer pestered my mind. Despite my steady stream of hardships, I felt energized, happy, calm, and confident all at once. Those feel-good endorphins released during physical activity possess the power to accomplish all of this and more.

I'm not here to suggest that this is the right time for you to take up an activity such as crossfit. In fact, if you're going through a particularly stressful time, I would recommend a more gentle form of movement as intense workouts can tax the adrenal glands. What I want you to do today is identify a form of physical activity that you'll look forward to. Here are a few stress-reducing ideas to get you started:

- Pilates or yoga
- Jogging
- Hiking with a friend
- Team sports
- Swimming
- Kayaking
- Gardening
- Playing tennis
- Taking a nature walk
- Dance (even if only at home with your kids!)
- Riding a bike

Do any of these ideas appeal to you? Whether you choose something from my list or discover your own favorite way of getting active, it's important to make time for it. Do you have thirty minutes available today to enjoy some mood-boosting movement? If not today, what about tomorrow? I want you to find three openings in your calendar over the course of the next week and schedule in that activity. If you want accountability and company, invite a friend to join you. And, if time is a problem, work in three ten-minute bursts of activity a day.

Once you get into the habit of practicing a regular physical activity that you enjoy and look forward to, you'll wonder how you ever survived without it. And on those particularly rough days, even five minutes of intentional movement can be enough to beat back depression or anxiety. The hard part is in choosing to do so even when you'd rather crawl in a hole, but you can do whatever you set your mind to do!

• • •

Be gentle on yourself as you

integrate each new stress-busting

tool into your life. The more you do

it, the easier it will become and the

better you'll feel about yourself.

• • •

EATING FOR LIFE

PART 1: MACRONUTRIENTS

• • •

"The food you eat can either be the safest and most powerful
form of medicine or the slowest form of poison."

ANN WIGMORE

• • •

Let's face it. When we're stressed, we want comfort. We want to feel like we're not alone. We want something to lessen the pain. Most of us tend to reach for something fatty or sugary, or both. We might even crave something nostalgic, something warm and satisfying that mama used to make. These foods register in the brain as a comfort and help us to feel less lonely, but are they really feeding us? If we continue to reach for our favorite comfort foods, we'll soon find ourselves crashing on the other side of that short-lived mood boost. Is it really worth it?

When we undergo periods of chronic stress, it's important to carefully consider not only our lifestyle and mindset choices but also our food choices. Our diet can actually cause our stress levels to either increase or decrease. We might not be able to change our circumstances immediately or make the sources of our stress go away, but we *can* support our mental, physical, and emotional health through nutrition.

While small amounts of stress hormones can be potentially life-saving if we legitimately need to run from danger, chronic elevated levels of these hormones can cause all kinds of health compromises. I've already shown you lots of ways to intentionally stimulate the release of stress-reducing hormones througout this book. Much of this has to do with our Primary Food, the food of life. But now I want to shift gears and talk about Secondary Food—the food on our plates.

Because there is a lot to cover and I don't want to overwhelm you, we'll spend two days on this topic of supporting wellness through nutrition. Today we'll take a look at our macronutrients and tomorrow we'll focus on micronutrients. If these terms are new to you, put simply macronutrients are nutrients we need in large amounts (carbs, protein, fats) and micronutrients are nutrients we need in smaller amounts (vitamins, minerals, antioxidants, etc.). Both are equally important.

I've done my best to incorporate what I believe to be key players in nutrition geared towards reducing stress and promoting a strong foundation for health in any season of life. This is by no means intended be a comprehensive nutrition guide or a substitute for a licensed practitioner. My goal here is to provide you with the basics and give you some tips on how to best support yourself from a nutrition standpoint. Please don't just take my word for it. Check in with your healthcare provider for individualized treatment.

Now let's get back to those macronutrients I mentioned. If you're an experienced gym enthusiast, then you probably know all about tracking your macros. You may have even used an app to track your intake of carbs, protein and fats as you aim to hit specific goals. Everyone has different nutritional needs and fitness targets. I'm not here to tell you what yours should be. But as long as you're in a season of working through hardships, I don't want you to worry so much (or at all) about your exact percentages. Keep your focus on choosing whole, unrefined foods from the best sources possible and leave tracking the macros for the bodybuilders.

CARBOHYDRATES

Yes, I want you to eat carbs. You know, that segment of the food pyramid that's gained a bad rap in this Paleo-popular, grain-free age. If you've cut the carbs thinking that you're going to be healthier or skinnier or happier (or all of the above), think again. We *need* healthy carbs. Carbohydrates actually reduce anxiety and depression by prompting the brain to make more serotonin while also delivering essential vitamins and minerals.

This isn't a free pass to go on a carb-eating frenzy, however. All carbohydrates are not created equal. While we can reap health benefits from wisely chosen simple carbohydrates (such as fruit, for example), overdoing it on any simple carb is only going to take us on an unwanted roller coaster ride as our blood sugar levels spike and crash.

Even still, a nutritious simple carb, such as an apple, is not the same as the quick-burning simple carb found in a soda. Any fruit with an edible skin is likely to contain a good amount of fiber. Fiber slows the breakdown of the sugar contained in fruit, meaning you're less likely to suffer from a post-apple crash. I can't say the same for a soda.

While small amounts of healthy, fiber-full simple carbs are good for us, we want to place our primary focus on the intake of complex carbohydrates. This type of carb provides us with a sustained source of energy as the sugars are slowly released into the bloodstream. Look for organic, sprouted whole grains as much as possible. Sprouted grains are both easier on the digestive system and more nutritionally available. By the way, if you've cut the carbs and have been struggling with depression, please consider adding complex carbs back into your diet and see if you don't notice an improvement.

Some favorite sources of complex carbohydrates at our house are:

• Brown rice

• Sweet potatoes

• Oatmeal (the more whole the better)

• Ezekiel bread

• Quinoa

• Beans

• Lentils

• Peas

PROTEIN

While many of us think of protein as that slice of the macronutrient pie chart that we focus on to build muscle and lose weight, protein also boasts incredible stress-reducing abilities. Protein is made up of amino acids, the building blocks of muscle tissue, hormones and neurotransmitters such as serotonin. Tryptophan is just one of those amino acids. Among the nine essential amino acids that our bodies don't produce, tryptophan is the one that is responsible for the well-known turkey coma.

What you might not know is that the "turkey coma" is a result of the serotonin that is produced by tryptophan. It's this release of serotonin that gives tryptophan it's ability to reduce cortisol levels, helping us to feel more calm and overall more agreeable after that Thanksgiving feast. But you don't have to eat turkey to enjoy the benefits of tryptophan. Other foods rich in this amino acid are nuts, seeds, tofu, fish, lentils, oats, beans, and eggs.

Eating protein alone isn't going to give us a tryptophan high, however. Carbohydrates and tryptophan work hand-in-hand to boost serotonin levels. While tryptophan makes blood sugar more accessible to our neurotransmitters, carbohydrates aid in the absorption of tryptophan. So, like I said earlier, I want you to eat carbs. We really do need protein *and* smart carbs.

Any form of protein is going to have a balancing effect on our blood sugar levels, which in turn provides mood balancing.[1] If you're pressed for time and feeling low on protein, be careful about the protein bars that are out there. Make sure you can pronounce everything on the label and that there aren't any isolates (meaning it's not a whole food). One of my favorite ways to get in an extra shot of protein is with either Sunwarrior Blend or the Sunwarrior Organic Meal for a more complete meal replacement in a pinch.

Other good sources of protein are:[2]

- Grass-fed beef

- Pastured chicken and turkey breast

- Wild salmon and tuna

- Greek yogurt (I recommend organic, whole fat)

- Cottage cheese

- Eggs

- Beans

- Lentils

- Nuts

- Quinoa

- Edamame

FATS

It's no surprise that the foods most of us crave during times of stress are high-fat. Comfort foods like ice cream, chocolate, pizza, and macaroni and cheese are full of saturated fats that offer a temporary calming effect along with a high caloric load. The downside of giving into these cravings, though, is that we are often left feeling tired and weighed down in more ways than one. Small amounts of the right types of fats, however, can be both healing and stress-reducing. While there is much that could be said about fats here, I want to focus on two important types of polyunsaturated fats.

You've most likely heard of Omega-3s and you may even take an Omega-3 supplement already. But do you know why they are one of your best friends while experiencing stress? Omega-3 essential fatty acids (or EFAs) are anti-inflammatory warriors. When you're stressed out, your inflammation levels rise thanks to stress hormones. Omega-3s support a healthy nervous system, mood regulation, and hormonal balance. They are *essential* to get from our food because our bodies don't produce them. I recommend Omega-3 supplementation and I'll tell you why in just a minute.

You've also probably heard of Omega-6s, another essential fatty acid that promotes health and is found mainly in our oils. In fact, our American diet is so loaded with Omega-6 fats in our salad dressings, conventionally raised meats, fried foods, potato chips, and pizza that we tend to get *too much* of this fatty acid. And that is why I do *not* recommend Omega-6 supplementation.

The reason why I'm bringing up Omega-6s here is because it's important to note that we should aim for a healthy ratio of Omega-6s to Omega-3s for optimal health. Seeing as how we already get plenty of Omega-6s in our American diet and typically not enough Omega-3s directly from food, Omega-3 supplementation is beneficial for lowering our ratio between the two. It's when this ratio is out of balance that we experience an increase in inflammation throughout the body and, as a result, higher rates of disease.[3]

I've heard from various practitioners that anything from a 5:1 ratio to a 2:1 ratio is ideal, but we don't need to get too worried about the exact numbers. It only makes sense that the lower the ratio, the healthier we're going to be. We simply need to be aware of our need to focus on increasing our intake of Omega-3s in our diet and supplements while steering clear of unhealthy sources of Omega-6s.

Personally, I trust a company called Nordic Naturals for fish oil which is high in Omega-3s. And where you get your fish oil from *does* matter. Rancid oil is not going to do you any favors. You'll know your oil is rancid if you're experiencing those awful fishy-flavored burps after taking the supplement. If that happens, please toss it and look for a better product.

Examples of foods high in Omega-3s are:[4]

- Wild salmon

- Sardines

- Grass-fed beef

- Flaxseeds

- Chia seeds

- Pistachios, walnuts, almonds

- Tuna

When it comes to cooking with oils and other fats, some work well with high temperatures and others are best reserved for unheated dressings and sauces. If you're cooking with an oil or butter and notice it sending up smoke signals, then it's already surpassed its smoke point. This high heat breaks the fat down and causes it to become rancid. Rancid oils are inflammatory to the body, so this is not going to serve us well in our health goals.

If you have questions about the proper use and storage of your favorite cooking oils, a simple Google search will yield all the information you need. Out of the most popular oils used, I suggest sticking to ghee (clarified butter) for the highest cooking temperatures (it also results in a lovely brown, crisp skin on your favorite roasted bird). Other fats commonly used that are generally safe for higher heats are safflower, grapeseed, and avocado oils. More delicate fats like sesame oil, virgin olive oil, and butter should be use with little to no heat.

RAISING AWARENESS

I realize that times of acute stress are not often conducive to making great strides in healthy eating habits. What I want to encourage you in most today is awareness. This might not be the best time to make drastic changes, but you'll benefit from any small adjustment you can make. If you've been in the habit of binging on certain unhealthy foods, try to avoid purchasing those items next time you're at the store. If those options aren't available when you have a weak moment, then you'll be spared from the temptation to indulge in something that isn't contributing to your wellness.

For now, consider what you've learned in this chapter and decide on one change you'd like to make starting today. Maybe you'd benefit most from taking an Omega-3 supplement. Or perhaps you might want to swap out an unhealthy carb or fat for a more healthy, stress-reducing version. Once this new change becomes a habit, you can consider making further adjustments down the road.

• • •

The goal in eating a

healthy diet is to reduce the

stress in your life, not add

to it. Keep it simple and

celebrate small victories!

• • •

EATING FOR LIFE

PART 2: MICRONUTRIENTS

• • •

"If you don't think your anxiety, depression, sadness and stress
impact your physical health, think again. All of these emotions
trigger chemical reactions in your body, which can lead to inflammation
and a weakened immune system. Learn how to cope, sweet friend.
There will always be dark days."

KRIS CARR, AUTHOR OF *CRAZY SEXY DIET*

• • •

While micronutrients don't contain any real calories, they do contain vital nutrients that are important players in the assault on stress, anxiety, and depression. A quote from one study connects stress with the reduction of necessary nutrients in the body:

Stress creates greater physiologic demands. Unhealthy eating patterns will only result in an increased level of stress, followed by further health problems if, in the future, the issues are not resolved. Prolonged stress increases the metabolic needs of the body and causes many other changes. The increased metabolism can also cause an increase in the use and excretion of many nutrients. Although stress alters nutrient needs, if marginally deficient in a nutrient, stress can make that deficiency even worse.[1]

Once again, I don't intend for this to be an exhaustive nutrition guide. I'm simply going to focus on those micronutrients that I feel are most beneficial in guarding the body against the damaging effects of stress. Let's take a look at some of the protective vitamins, minerals, antioxidants, and phytochemicals we're consuming in the foods we eat.

VITAMIN C

There are lots of antioxidant-rich foods available to reduce stress while also supplying us with a healthy dose of vitamin C, a stress-busting antioxidant. It's important to note that the adrenal glands contain the largest concentration of vitamin C in the body.[2] The adrenal glands in particular take a serious hit when we're under stress. Excessive demand on our adrenals can potentially weaken our immune system as our vitamin C stores are used up in the production of stress hormones. Our goal is to support our adrenals and add in as many vitamin C-rich foods as possible to avoid becoming depleted.

Because vitamin C is a water-soluble vitamin and our bodies don't produce it, it's up to us to take in a sufficient supply through our diet and, if necessary, supplementation. As far as supplements go, I recommend that you avoid ascorbic acid, a synthetic form of vitamin C.

Not only can it cause stomach irritation, but it can also do more harm than good in the long run. When you look for a vitamin C supplement, you want a whole vitamin derived from real food. Ascorbic acid is not that, so please check your labels carefully.

By the way, those megadoses of vitamin C aren't necessarily doing you any good, either. Because it is a water-soluble vitamin, excessive intake is only going to end up in your urine. It's better to take smaller doses throughout the day.

Some good sources of vitamin C are:[3]

- Guava, papaya, mango and pineapple (for my friends back in Hawaii)

- Bell peppers (each color offers a different antioxidant)

- Kiwi

- Oranges and grapefruit

- Berries

- Broccoli

- Kale and other leafy greens

VITAMIN B

B is for "bounce back" where this vitamin is concerned. One study showed that a vitamin B complex caused significant improvement in the reduction of stress and anxiety in those who experienced a natural disaster.[4] This is due to the fact that vitamin B helps us recover from bouts of stress more quickly, making us more resilient. One of the best ways to support the nervous system is to maintain healthy levels of this important vitamin. We want to keep our neurotransmitters signaling the release of those happy hormones, right? Vitamin B helps make that happen.

Like vitamin C, vitamin B is also a water-soluble vitamin. This means that we need a steady daily intake from our food and, if needed, supplementation. It's common to be deficient specifically in folate (vitamin B12), which can lead to all sorts of health issues such as fatigue, depression, digestive disorders, and heart disease.[5] Those who eat a plant-based diet are more likely to be deficient in B12, a nutrient that is derived primarily from animal products. Depending upon your own dietary preferences, you may want to consider consulting with a physician about your unique requirements.

When looking for a supplement, I recommend a B-complex rather than isolated B vitamins because they work together synergistically. Also, read the label carefully. Naturally occurring folate is preferred to folic acid, a synthetic form of folate. This is especially true for those with the MTHFR gene mutation as the body's ability to convert folic acid into a useable form is reduced. Because folic acid is synthetic, it requires an additional metabolic process in the liver before it can be used by the body.[6] Folate is our friend particularly during times of stress as it produces dopamine, that wonderful pleasure-inducing brain chemical.

Vitamin B can be found in foods such as:[7]

• Liver

• Salmon

- Tuna

- Eggs

- Brewer's yeast

- Lentils

- Black beans

- Sunflower seeds

- Spinach

VITAMIN D

Vitamin D is called the sunshine vitamin because the sun is our best source of this important micronutrient. When skin is exposed to the sun, vitamin D is produced and sent to the liver and kidneys. Vitamin D is actually the only vitamin that our body produces on its own. However, it can be a challenge to produce enough vitamin D from sun exposure alone, particularly in the cooler months. Because of this, the majority of Americans can benefit from supplementation.

Unlike water-soluble vitamins B and C, vitamin D is a fat-soluble vitamin. This means that it isn't flushed out of the body when there is an excess. Instead, vitamin D dissolves in fat and is stored up in our liver and fatty tissues.[8] While vitamin D can be tolerated in higher amounts than other fat-soluble vitamins, caution should still be exercised where supplementation is concerned. Excess amounts can be harmful.

I recommend having your vitamin D level tested and choosing your unique dosage with the help of a health practitioner. You can also order a home test kit from *zrtlab.com*. The Vitamin D Council recommends adults take 5,000 IU/day of a vitamin D supplement in order to achieve the ideal level of 80-100 ng/ml.[9] Again, it's important to have your levels monitored by a physician.

So why is it so important for us to maintain healthy vitamin D levels? Well, vitamin D is a big player in the reduction of depression and anxiety. But vitamin D is more than just a vitamin, it functions as a steroid hormone and plays an important role in the protection against certain cancers as well as the development of diabetes and heart disease. A major role of vitamin D is the maintenance of balanced calcium levels, which in turn supports strong bones.

If you've been drinking milk thinking that you're supporting bone health, take a look at this. Pasteurized milk is linked to both calcium and vitamin D deficiency disorders. It's true. There are only trace amounts of naturally-occurring vitamin D found in milk, raw or pasteurized. Milk is usually fortified with man-made D2, a form of vitamin D that isn't nearly as absorbable as D3. So if you want to ensure healthy calcium levels, the best way to do that is not with a glass a milk, but rather through sufficient vitamin D3 intake.

There aren't a lot of options for food sources of vitamin D, but here are a few:[10]

- Cod liver oil

- Fatty fish (salmon, mackerel, tuna and sardines)

- Raw dairy products

- Egg yolks from pastured hens

- Mushrooms

- Liver from grass-fed animals

ANTIOXIDANTS AND PHYTOCHEMICALS

You may have heard the saying "eat a rainbow." This colorful reminder to eat a varied a diet is for good reason. Every color of the rainbow offers a unique set of antioxidants, those naturally occurring substances that protect against cellular damage. Generally speaking, the foods with the darkest hues contain the most antioxidants. While I'm mainly talking about dark foods like blueberries, blackberries, and purple cabbage, I'll also include a popular comfort food in this category: chocolate.

I'm not here to take your favorite chocolate bar away from you. In fact, you can keep your chocolate as long as you enjoy it in moderation. Dark chocolate in particular is both emotionally *and* chemically beneficial. The simple act of savoring that piece of chocolate gets the serotonin flowing. That's right, just the feeling of relishing a treat stimulates the release of serotonin. Additionally, dark chocolate relieves stress at the molecular level thanks to high levels of antioxidants. So there you go, you can have your chocolate and eat it, too.

Phytonutrients are those nutrients found in plants that protect both plants and consumers of plants alike from environmental damage. These plant-derived compounds serve us in many ways, including the reduction of inflammation in the body. Eating a rainbow will ensure that we are using our food to fight in our defense, improving our response to stress and fending off disease.

Foods high in both antioxidants and phytonutrients include:[11]

- Goji berries, wild blueberries, cranberries, blackberries and elderberries

- Dark chocolate

- Nuts and seeds

- Artichokes

- Cilantro

- Leafy greens

- Ancient grains

- Beans and legumes

WHOLE FOOD NUTRITION

Ultimately, the best source of any nutrient is from whole foods. Eating a varied diet full of raw, colorful veggies, whole sprouted grains, and clean protein sources will cover the vast majority of our nutritional requirements. But during times of stress or illness, it may be necessary to supplement as our nutrients are either depleted or poorly absorbed. Maybe we can't make stress go away completely, but we can support the body nutritionally to minimize the damaging effects of stress as much as possible.

Please don't worry about completely revamping your diet today. I don't necessarily recommend that you go out and buy every supplement I've mentioned, either. As you continue incorporating new healthy habits into your diet and lifestyle, be sure to stay in a place of peace. If a sudden, drastic change best suits your personality and brings you peace, then I'm not here to stop you from doing that. In my experience, those who are most successful at making lasting changes are the ones who gradually allow their healthy choices to crowd out those old habits that haven't been doing them any favors.

I encourage you to quiet yourself and tune into your body, soul, and spirit today. Listen closely and you'll probably know what one new addition is most important for you to begin focusing on. Start with that and, over time, gradually add to your new nutrition plan.

• • •

Take it slow. Within a few

months of focusing on proper

nutrition, you'll look back and

see the rewards you've reaped

in your health along the way.

• • •

BOOSTING GUT HEALTH

• • •

"Anything that affects the gut always affects the brain."

DR. CHARLES MAJORS

• • •

As we continue to focus on ways to boost resilience, we cannot skip talking about gut health. Our ability to absorb the nutrients we've discussed in the past couple of chapters is directly connected to our gut health. It doesn't make much sense to focus on boosting nutrition if our gut is in such a weakened state that we're unable to properly absorb the nutrients from our food and supplements.

Our ability to bounce back from stress is directly tied to a delicate balance of good and bad bacteria in the gut. In fact, a whole slew of health issues can be attributed to an imbalance in our gut flora, otherwise known as dysbiosis.

According to Dr. Sara Gottfried, you may be suffering from dysbiosis if you exhibit five or more of the following symptoms:[1]

- Frequent gas or bloating on most days of the week

- Cramping, urgency, and/or mucus in your stool once per week

- Brain fog, anxiety, or depression

- Food sensitivities

- Missing micronutrients

- Chronic bad breath

- Loose stool, diarrhea, constipation, or a combination

- Diagnosis of Irritable Bowel Syndrome (IBS)

- History of "stomach bugs," gastroenteritis, and/or food poisoning

- History of prolonged antibiotics such as for acne or sinusitis

- Carbohydrate intolerance, particularly after eating fiber and/or beans

- Fatigue or low energy

- Use of antacids for heartburn, reflux, or hiatal hernia

- Autoimmunity, or an autoimmune condition such as Hashimoto's thyroiditis, psoriasis, or multiple sclerosis

- Sinus congestion

Are you surprised? Well, allow me to share with you an example from my own life. From the time I was a teen all the way through my mid-thirties, I suffered from several chronic health issues most of which seemed to be entirely disconnected. Among them were hormonal imbalance, infertility, irritability, heartburn, and other related digestive troubles as well as chronic and severe eczema, allergies, and insomnia. After battling infertility for six years (and conceiving three babies with the help of fertility drugs), we "randomly" conceived our surprise baby girl while participating in a cleanse that required me to eat a gluten-free diet.

I didn't make the connection between the two until a couple of years later when Dr. Ronda finally convinced me to try giving up gluten. I followed her advice in hopes of seeing my miserable eczema clear up. By this point I was desperate enough to give up my beloved home-made bread habit and, within a few gluten-free months, my eczema did at last go away. But what surprised me most was that, in time, every single one of my other chronic health issues also went away. All I had done differently was give up a food that I was intolerant to, a food that had likely been creating an upset in my gut health for decades. My list of ailments later returned with a vengeance a couple of years later due to high levels of chronic stress. But you already know that story.

So often in modern medicine today our whole person is split up into isolated parts. We see one specialist for our grumpy gallbladder, another one for our bad knee, and yet another physician for that persistent rash. And then if we exhibit any emotional or psychological struggles, we are sent to a whole 'nother set of experts who have been specifically trained to manage those supposed non-physical issues. Perhaps you've experienced this as I have while trying to resolve a multitude of ailments at once.

It's great that we have specialists to turn to when we need them. With all of this specialization going on, however, it can oftentimes be difficult to find a physician who can look at us and make a connection between all of our systems and innerworkings. What if that mental health challenge we're exhibiting doesn't actually need medication? It could, in fact, be our body's way of telling us that we have an imbalance in our gut bacteria, or microbiota. The same could be said for that relentless eczema or indigestion, both symptoms of a possible imbalance in the gut. Every part of our being is affected by this ratio of good critters versus bad critters within us.

The gut and the brain are talking to each other all day long via a direct line between the two. In fact, during fetal development the brain and the gut (aka "second brain") begin as one and the same, only to divide later in the development process. Keeping in line with our goal of reclaiming hope and health, I want to focus on ways to promote optimal health in this second brain as it relates to both physical and emotional wellness.

First of all, there are a number of environmental factors that have the potential to wreak havoc on the healthy bacteria in the gut, leaving us in a state of dysbiosis.[2] Among them are:

- Stress

- Unhealthy diet (sugar and processed foods)

- Eating foods we're intolerant to

- Birth control pills and other hormones

- Antibiotics

- Chlorine

In one study, it was proven that increased levels of the beneficial bacteria *Bifidobacterium* contributes to stress resilience and may also play a key role in the prevention and therapeutic treatment of depression and other mood disorders.[3] These probiotic microbes also have the ability to cause immune system changes, increasing immune function and demonstrating anti-inflammatory actions.

What all of this boils down to in simple terms is this: sufficient levels of certain probiotics foster increased physical and emotional health. That sounds like a great tool to employ in our quest for hope and health, wouldn't you agree? Here are some ways to encourage a healthy microbiome in the gut:

- **Eat fermented foods.*** Naturally fermented pickles are my favorite, but others like sauerkraut, kimchi and kefir are also great choices.

- **Drink kombucha.*** This probiotic drink is now widely available in stores. It's also easy and inexpensive to make at home.

- **Eat more fiber.** Take in 33-39 grams of dietary fiber per day, especially plant fiber. The good critters are fed by the fiber (or prebiotics) in our diet.

- **Take up gardening.** Any chance to get your hands dirty exposes you to friendly bacteria, offering immune-boosting benefits.

- **Relax on the antibacterial products.** Exposure to a variety of bacteria actually strengthens the immune system and supports a healthy gut.

- **Rest and digest.** It's important to eat in a relaxed state. Doing so encourages the release of important digestive enzymes, supporting better nutrient absorption and a more balanced microbiome.

- **Take a probiotic supplement.** There are mixed reviews on the benefits of probiotic supplementation. I do believe that it can help maintain a healthy gut, so I recommend a Garden of Life supplement that I take called Mood+. This product contains ten strains of *Lactobacillus* and six strains of *Bifidobacterium* as well as a powerful adaptogenic herb that helps us cope with stress, ashwagandha. Unlike many probiotic supplements, this one requires no refrigeration.

*Note that probiotic foods may cause a problem for those with bacterial overgrowth. Pay careful attention to how you feel when you eat these foods. If you feel excessively bloated or ill, try backing off on fermented foods and try other gut health-boosting tools.

As you surely know by now, stress takes a serious toll on gut health. No matter what type of gut imbalance you may be dealing with, any form of stress reduction is going to promote healing and balance. As you continue to practice the tools described within these pages, both of your brains will thank you with improved mood and digestion, a stronger immune system, better energy, and more.

. . .

You're not going to be able

to turn your microbiome

around in a day, but consistent

awareness and implementation of

a gut-friendly lifestyle will have

you well on your way to enjoying

all the benefits of a healthy gut.

. . .

SLEEPING WELL

• • •

"The best bridge between despair and
hope is a good night's sleep."

E. JOSEPH COSSMAN

• • •

While sleep and I have not been on good terms for most of my life, I've made huge strides in this department in recent years. To those of you who struggle terribly with achieving the restorative type of sleep we all need to thrive, I get it. I know how frustrating it is to lie in bed night after night wishing for sleep to come, only to toss and turn until it's at last time to drag your exhausted self through another day. I know because I lived like this for over thirteen years of my life. My husband, on the other hand, was a fantastic sleeper!

I'll never forget the second morning of our honeymoon in late October of 1997. Peter woke up as refreshed as ever only to find me curled up on the floor in front of the fire in our little Baywood Park condo. I hadn't slept a wink and, instead, spent the better part of those hours reserved for sleep and restoration crying, imagining spending the rest of my life watching Peter sleep without being able to enter into it myself. I envisioned the life ahead of us and wondered how I would ever be the kind of wife I wanted to be if I couldn't even manage to sleep well.

I was tired and miserable, Peter was mostly patient and understanding, and that's the way we lived life until I discovered that gluten intolerance was the root cause of my chronic insomnia thirteen long years later. Most people didn't understand how severe my battle with sleep was, and those who did deemed me the highest-functioning insomniac they knew. And that's without being a coffee drinker! Mom guilt ridiculed me as I often woke up in the morning only after Peter had seen our boys off to school. What kind of mother didn't get up with her kids in the morning? That wasn't the kind of mom I wanted to be, but when I couldn't fall asleep until five o'clock in the morning most nights (or mornings, rather), I couldn't see a way around it.

Melatonin did nothing for me. Ambien gave me frightening amnesia and didn't leave me feeling any more rested than before. Going to sleep at the same time every night and attempting to wake up at the same time every morning didn't help at all. I'm pretty sure I tried every sleep cure known to man without any lasting success. It's now widely known that gluten intolerance, and any food sensitivity for that matter, can lead to chronic insomnia. This isn't the time to get into why that is, but I'll just say that if you struggle with sleep as I did, please find a practitioner to help pinpoint potential food sensitivities for you.

Aside from food sensitivities, there are many other conditions that can cause disruptions in our ability to achieve deep sleep. Anxiety, depression, restless leg syndrome, sleep apnea, pain, hormonal imbalances, substance abuse, and digestive troubles are among some of the most common thieves of our restorative sleep. Some of the not-so-fun side effects of sleep deprivation are chronic fatigue, reduced immune function, higher rates of depression, difficulty regulating mood and emotions, and trouble concentrating. All in all, it's just plain impossible to thrive in the absence of a healthy sleep pattern.

Today I'm going to outline for you many of the pathways to better sleep I've discovered over the years as well as some new strategies I learned at a seminar taught by Dr. John D. Preston.[1] I suggest that you have a highlighter handy as you go through these tips for achieving better rest. Be sure to highlight any key strategies that you may want to incorporate into your life in the near future.

- **Begin winding down 2–3 hours before bed.** Avoid any exciting movies, sporting events or anything else that might stimulate the release of stress hormones too close to bedtime. This might seem difficult or even drastic at first, but it's a price worth paying for restorative sleep.

- **Avoid engaging in any evening arguments.** Keep your evenings calm. Conflict before bedtime is only going to ramp up those stress hormones and prevent you from getting the rest you need to reset your already fragile emotions.

- **Treat any underlying sleep disorders.** If you suspect that you may have a sleep disorder, seek out a specialist to help you resolve that. Be sure to look at and work towards healing root causes rather than only applying bandages over symptoms.

- **Reduce caffeine intake.** Caffeine has a half-life of between five and six hours. While I'd suggest cutting it out completely for those who struggle with sleep, at the very least keep your caffeine intake under 500 mg per morning and at zero after noon.

- **Wean off of any sleep-disturbing substances.** Besides caffeine, other drugs such as narcotics, nicotine, tranquilizers, and alcohol can keep you from sleeping well. (Please wean off of these substances gradually and, if needed, under the supervision of a physician.)

- **Ditch the sleeping pills.** Yes, it feels awesome to not lie awake all night when you've suffered with insomnia for long periods of time, but those sleeping pills are likely not doing you any favors. Research shows that sleeping pills can actually decrease sleep efficiency and, while they may keep you knocked out all night, you don't actually achieve significant levels of deep sleep.

- **Have your thyroid hormones tested.** Thyroid dysfunction is very common and often overlooked as a source of sleep disturbance. Balancing thyroid hormones can be a delicate dance, so please consult a knowledgeable naturopathic physician or functional medicine doctor for support.

- **Establish a regular exercise routine.** Aerobic exercise can help regulate sleep as long as it's performed more than three hours prior to bedtime.

- **Bore yourself sleepy.** Do whatever it is that bores you most in those final moments of the day. Read dull poetry or long biblical genealogies. Listen to an uninteresting audiobook. Or try out the Sleep With Me podcast on iTunes, "a lulling, droning, boring bedtime story to distract your racing mind." (You might think this is silly, but it surprisingly works quite well for me!)

- **Perform a brain dump.** If racing thoughts or worries are keeping you awake, get out a pen and paper and write out the first worries that come to your mind. Then set it aside and let your mind relax.

- **Listen to Pzizz.** Check it out on iTunes. According to *pzizz.com*, they "utilize effective psychoacoustic principles to create beautiful dreamscapes that will help you fall asleep fast, stay asleep, and wake up feeling refreshed."

- **Sleep cool.** To achieve deep sleep, the body must cool down by two to three degrees. Most experts say that the ideal room temperature for deep sleep is sixty-eight degrees.

- **Limit use of melatonin.** Yes, it's a naturally occurring sleep hormone. No, that doesn't mean it's harmless. Melatonin use can actually throw a wrench in your natural circadian rhythm. Do not take it in excess of 0.5 mg per night unless under medical supervision. Frequent use can increase depression and even destabilize bipolar disorder. Avoid completely with children as this can affect the development of their sex organs.

- **Screen out blue light.**[2] Even as I write this, I'm using a blue light-reducing app that causes the color of my computer's display to adapt to the time of day, making it appear warm at night and like sunlight during the day. This app is available at *justgetflux.com*. Some computers and phones come with built-in apps for this purpose.

- **Wear amber lenses.** If you must look at a screen in the evening hours, try wearing amber lenses to cut out the over-stimulating blue light. To be effective, though, the lenses must screen out 90% of blue light (most only cut out 10%).

- **Keep it dark and quiet.** Block out any source of light or distracting noise from your bedroom. Even the glowing light from digital alarm clocks can cause a disturbance in your natural sleep cycle.

- **Turn in early.** The stress hormone cortisol should reach its lowest level between midnight and four o'clock in the morning. When you stay awake past midnight, you are forcing your cortisol levels into an unnatural rhythm which, in turn, prevents your body from being able to use vitamin D. (Remember, you need sunlight to make it and sleep to use it.) Keep your body and brain strong by getting to sleep well before midnight.

If anyone tends towards of the life of a night owl, it's me—just ask my earlybird husband. Even though I enjoy my quiet evening hours immensely (you would, too, if you had six kids at home), I have learned enough about the importance of establishing a healthy sleep pattern that I make greater efforts to turn out the lights as close to ten o'clock as possible. My dear husband is usually sawing logs by then, anyway. When you struggle with the self-discipline required to get to bed at a reasonable time, remind yourself that practically every situation seems better after a little rest.

No matter what you may be going through at this present time or what you may go through in the future, you'll absolutely be serving yourself and your loved ones best if you're well-rested. If sleep has been a struggle for you, I hope that one or more of the tips I've listed will help you achieve better rest. As with everything else, don't feel like you have to tackle all of these adjustments in a day.

• • •

Begin today with whichever

sleep strategy you feel will serve

you most effectively. In time, your

natural rhythm will kick in and

you'll soon be reaping all the

restorative rewards of deep sleep.

• • •

Pursuing a Passion

• • •

"Passion is energy. Feel the power that comes from focusing on what excites you."

OPRAH WINFREY

• • •

Would you believe me if I told you that I began my college career as a marine biology major? It's true. I had been obsessed with bottlenose dolphins since the fourth grade and entertained the possibility of becoming a dolphin trainer for many years. As a teenager I had the opportunity to attend a marine biology camp during which we got to explore the tide pools and study a bit at Humboldt State University's marine biology lab. I *loved* it.

Upon graduation from high school, I thought I knew exactly what I would do when I grew up. But as you've probably learned yourself many times over by now, things don't always work out like we think they will.

Seven years and a few degree major changes later, I finally earned my B.A. Even still, it wasn't until thirteen years later that I discovered my true passion and at last knew what I wanted to be when I "grew up." This is the period of time I wrote about in chapter two when I discovered the Institute for Integrative Nutrition. My life was coming apart at the seams, but it was my passion for wellness that ended up playing a key role in getting me through that stormy season. As I mentioned earlier, I literally went from hopelessness to hopeFULLness in a matter of weeks. Tapping into my passion proved to be immeasurably powerful.

If you currently find yourself smack dab in the middle of perhaps your worst nightmare, I realize that the idea of pursuing a passion might seem far-fetched if not completely ridiculous. Not knowing your particular circumstances, I can't decide that for you. All I can say is that, from my personal experience, choosing to go after my dreams even in the midst of my life's greatest storm made a world of difference. My passion became the primary vehicle that carried me through the storm with a sense of meaningful purpose.

Ironically, it was the storm itself that revealed my life's passion to me. Had I not suffered physically for many years, I might not have ever discovered how truly passionate I was about holistic wellness. And had I not witnessed first-hand the miraculous transformation that naturopathic medicine brought about in Peter, I might not have become such a convinced believer in the power of holistic healing modalities.

How did I know that I'd discovered my passion? Because something deep inside of me woke up! I uncovered fresh energy and an excitement about my future that I'd never before experienced. My circumstances hadn't changed, yet I woke up every morning feeling happy and hopeful. When I began my courses at IIN, I couldn't get enough. The time *flew by* while I listened to the lectures by the world's top health and wellness experts. Learning about various holistic healing modalities fed my soul on a level that breathed new life into every part of me.

It's been five years since that time and I haven't stopped learning. My passion for wellness has only continued to grow stronger as time goes on. That's how I know it is truly *is* my passion. But this health and wellness field that has brought me so much life might not excite you so much, and that's okay. When you step into *your* passion, if you haven't already, you'll recognize it immediately.

There's a lot of talk in our culture today about going after our dreams and following our hearts. I do believe that this is an important message, however I have also seen a number of people grow discouraged as they struggle to either pinpoint their dreams and passions or fail to see them come to fruition. So let's not over-complicate things, okay? We all know that life can be complicated enough as it is.

If you don't know what your life's passion is today, please don't stress over it. I just want you to be on the lookout for those moments when you start to feel yourself come alive. Pay attention to what makes your heart sing. What brings tears to your eyes? What feeds your soul and consistently energizes you? (No, I'm not talking about your favorite latte here!) What did you love to do as a child?

Some of you have been waiting for permission to pursue your passions. For whatever reason, you've put your dreams on hold. Maybe it just hasn't felt like the right timing. Perhaps you feel guilty or even selfish for following your heart during a time when life isn't necessarily at a high point. I know that, for me, I wrestled with this very thing. I didn't know if it was okay to chase after my dreams in a season of life that already seemed to require more than I had to give. My husband wasn't well. Our marriage felt like a never-ending roller coaster. Our children were young and demanded all of me. My health was in the gutter. The cards were absolutely stacked against me.

It was because of this desperate place I was in that I felt I had nothing to lose. There was never going to be a perfect time to take the leap. I had the full support of my husband and that was the only green light I needed. It was totally crazy and made complete sense all at once. Sometimes going after our dreams looks exactly like that. It might be complicated at times, but it's worth going after if it nourishes you like my career in the health and wellness field has nourished me.

In those moments when I've had mom guilt try to tell me that I should set my dreams aside and focus solely on my children and my home, I have to remind myself that I'm a better wife and mom when I'm doing what I love. One of my childhood dreams was absolutely to become a wife and a mother. Years of battling infertility threatened to squelch that dream, but here I am today with no lack of children!

I want to be the kind of mom who pursues her passions alongside her children. It's true that my time is more divided, but I am happier, healthier, and more fulfilled as a person when I'm doing what I feel called to do. As a result, I fully believe that my entire family reaps the rewards of my choices as long as I continue to keep them at the top of my priority list.

We don't have to choose between our families and our dreams.

I challenge you to find a way to create a little space in your day to do something just because you love it. It might be something you've done since you were a child. This could like look like trying a new hobby or reading a book you've been wanting to read. It could even be something so simple as coloring in a coloring book or plunking out a tune on a neglected instrument. If it brings you joy and revives your soul, then do it.

• • •

Pursuing your passion is not an

all-or-nothing thing. Keep it simple

if you must, but find something

that feeds your soul like nothing else.

As you do, your days will begin

to look a little bit brighter.

• • •

Day 30

BOUNCING FORWARD

• • •

"Trauma doesn't have to defeat you. It can be a
perfect opportunity for growth. Don't just make a comeback.
Use it as a catalyst forward."

MATT MCWILLIAMS

• • •

While on vacation in my former home of Mammoth Lakes, California this past summer, I took three of our children to visit their favorite local bookstore, The Booky Joint. I love the smell, the sense of fresh inspiration, and everything else that comes with being in a room full of books. Scanning the shelves and admiring the more impressive covers, one book in particular jumped out at me. I picked up *Option B: Facing Adversity, Building Resilience and Finding Joy* by Sheryl Sandberg and Adam Grant. This title obviously aligned well with the heart of my own book-in-progress, so I bought it.

Once the kids and I had completed our purchases and left the store armed with new books and art supplies, we headed up the hill to Twin Lakes. Finding a quiet spot near the water, we spread out our blankets, snacks, reading and art materials and together we feasted. I read aloud to them while they put their new pencils and art paper to good use.

I soon discovered that I was reading the story of a young widow and single mother like myself. Connecting deeply with Sheryl's story, I related intimately with her entire process of walking through grief with her brokenhearted children. She had lost her forty-seven-year-old husband, Dave, to a sudden heart attack while on vacation with friends in Mexico. It was within the pages of Sheryl's book that the reason for my writing of *this* book was spelled out for me.

> "*After undergoing a hardship, people have new knowledge to offer those who go through similar experiences. It is a unique source of meaning because it does not just give our lives purpose—it gives our suffering purpose. People help where they've been hurt so that their wounds are not in vain.*"[1]

When I read this, I couldn't help but break down and cry. It was all true. So much of my drive to complete this book has been wrapped up in assigning purpose not only to my own suffering, but also to the suffering of our entire family. I don't want one single bit of it to be in vain. If sharing what I've learned from all I've been through can help even one person break free from trauma's debilitating aftermath, then somehow it feels worth it. That's where you come in.

My hope for you is that, having read this book for the past thirty days or so, you will have the tools to help you bounce forward from the storm you've endured. What I learned in *Option B* is that post-traumatic growth is a real thing and it's possible for all of us. My completion of this book is part of my own bouncing forward, my way of growing through the trials I've experienced. Bouncing forward will look different for each of us, but generally it looks like growth that likely wouldn't have occurred had we not walked through fire.

A friend of mine went through three and a half years of cancer treatment with her young son, Kicker. I remember how news of his diagnosis spread like wildfire through our community and brought her and her husband to their knees. Despite this shocking blow, I knew that this family would rise to the challenge. And they did exactly that.

By the end of Kicker's lengthy treatment, the KICKcancER Movement was in full swing educating and empowering families on nutrition and natural wellness throughout cancer treatment and beyond. Not only did Kicker thrive during his treatment and receive a cancer-free bill of health, but his family supported hundreds of others going through a similar battle to thrive as well. That's exactly what bouncing forward looks like. And by the way, you can learn more about what the KICKcancER Movement has to offer families affected by pediatric cancer at *kickcancermovement.org*.[2]

Thankfully for this family, their story did not end in tragedy. But for many of us, tragedy has either occurred already or will occur in the future. We can't do a thing to change that, but we *can* choose how we respond in the face of unavoidable calamity. Painful emotions will come and go, but these feelings don't have to decide our futures for us. Bouncing forward is a choice we each have to make for ourselves.

I couldn't write this book without thinking of the many inspiring women I am blessed to call my friends. As you continue in your personal journey beyond the pages of this book, you may have days that require some additional inspiration. When those days come, I invite you to turn to the last section of this book and meet a few of my thriving friends. These women have each walked through hell and back in various ways, but I've watched them bounce forward in spite of all the odds. I believe that their stories will inspire you to do the same.

It's in the seemingly small decisions we make each and every day that we choose to not only bounce back, but to bounce forward and thrive despite our circumstances. It is my sincere hope that this book will play a part in helping you do just that.

• • •

I look forward to hearing

about how you choose to

bounce forward. The world

needs what you have to give.

• • •

Section
THREE

• • •

MY THRIVING
FRIENDS

Corina

• • •

When my husband was first diagnosed with Huntington's Disease, a genetic brain disorder that gradually kills nerve cells in the brain, I thought my life was over. It was as if time stopped completely. We had seven children who depended on us. I couldn't begin to imagine what our future might look like.

At the time, we lived in a spiritual environment that embraced miracles and physical healing. This type of miracle was what we hoped and prayed for. But as time went on, my husband was not only NOT getting healed, he seemed to be getting worse. The grief, pain, and disappointment that I was feeling was intense. The "what if's" racing through my mind were grueling. This diagnosis felt like a death sentence.

I was always taught not to ask the question "Why?" but instead to ask, "How?" It's that principle that I have been able to hold onto for the last decade as I walk out this disease together with my husband. Prior to his illness, I would think of the word grace in the same way I might think of something small or frail. I've come to discover that grace isn't either of those things. Grace is the grease, so to speak, that keeps the wheels turning. Grace is the thing that I have been able to lean on one day at a time and, sometimes, one hour or even one minute at a time. This type of tangible grace provides me with the powerful ability to get up every morning, the energy to go about each day without showing the wear of the warfare on my face. It's not always easy, but it's always possible.

A year after my husband's diagnosis, I enrolled in midwifery school. The future was feeling very uncertain, but one thing I was sure of was that I wasn't going to stop living because I was afraid. I was not going to kill my dreams simply because I was fearful of never being able to accomplish them. And so I made a choice. Day by day for the next four years, I chipped away at my dream of becoming a midwife. Passing my boards and receiving my license was life-changing for me. I knew that there was now nothing I could not do.

When people first meet me, I rarely tell them of my struggles and they usually can't tell what I'm going through by looking at me. You could say I am wearing "everyday grace" on my face. This doesn't mean I don't have my bad days, but it does mean that I have learned how to stay in the present moment and to not be so hard on myself. We need to learn to extend ourselves the same grace we would all give our friends. It's necessary and perfectly okay to feel what you need to feel, just don't get stuck there. Learn to lean into grace.

Gwyne

"When the grip of darkness seems to snuff out any light, take heart my friend. The sun will surely rise again."

• • •

It was "go" time! Contractions were steady and growing in intensity the morning of October 11, 2010. We rushed to the hospital, prepared to deliver a perfectly healthy baby girl. It had been a normal pregnancy with no concerns, so you can imagine our shock when the doctor soberly announced, "I see the heart, but it's not moving. I'm sorry but your baby has passed."

The power of the Holy Spirit was truly present when those words were spoken. Instead of crying out with a guttural scream, I immediately felt a surge of faith rise in my heart to believe in God's power to heal our baby.

We navigated the next six hours of labor with many friends coming to pray and believe with us for her healing. She finally came. Our Eden Iyana was now in my arms and songs and scriptures were read over her, beckoning life, Life, LIFE!

As time passed, we didn't know what else to do. We cried out, "Lord, help!" Soon afterward, I heard Him say, "She's alive—with Me!"

It was then I felt the sucker punch of devastating loss to my gut. But once again, amid such great pain, the power of the Holy Spirit moved upon us, enabling us to let her go.

Oftentimes I experience a spiritual battle in the days and moments that follow an event as intense as this one. The familiar war rages on in my mind where doubt and fear confront me. Flurries of thoughts threaten to consume me with tormenting "what if's" and tempt me to vow, "I will never do THAT again."

A scripture I hold onto during these times reminds me to take every tormenting thought captive. "We are destroying speculations and every lofty thing raised up against the knowledge of God, and we are taking every thought captive to the obedience of Christ" (2 Cor. 10:5, NASB).

This same "lofty and speculative" spirit is precisely what captured my attention after Eden died. It wanted to cast a future of hopelessness upon me and keep me bound up by anxiety and torment. I entertained thoughts like, "Your body is now damaged and you'll never get pregnant again." I felt a wave of panic each time a pregnancy test gave me a negative result. Defeating thoughts had a stranglehold on my heart.

A friend helped me expose those negative thought patterns that weren't my own and bring them into the light. Through the freeing act of repentance (which means "to change one's mind") and receiving prayer, these unhealthy thought patterns were cut off, allowing the HOPE that was buried in me to spring forth and revive my soul! Faith arose to lead me to LIFE in the darkest moment I had ever known.

I encourage you to CHOOSE to believe He is good. CHOOSE to find life in His Word. CHOOSE to talk to someone. CHOOSE to speak against those lies that seek to cut off your breath and life, even if you feel like you have no more breath in you. He is our Helper and Counselor. Our God never leaves or forsakes us—NEVER, my dear friend. I am learning to hope in Him, not in my circumstances or feelings.

• • •

"Now hope does not disappoint, because the love of God has been poured out in our hearts by the Holy Spirit who was given to us."

ROMANS 5:5, NKJV

Karen

...

I was only fourteen years old when I was diagnosed with polyarticular rheumatoid juvenile arthritis, a very aggressive disease that can affect many joints at one time.

I will never forget sitting in that cold gray and white doctor's office awaiting six months of test results to finally identify what was causing this endless pain. I stared at the tile floor as they told me there was no cure.

"You'll have to be on medications that we hope will give you some quality of life. Because of the medications you'll be dependent upon, you'll likely never be able to get off of them in order to have children. You'll eventually be in a wheelchair. There's a small chance that you could

enter remission in your early twenties, but for most this is something that becomes a lifelong ailment."

My world came crashing down in a day.

Fast forward twenty-six years and three children later. I'm living as best as I can despite experiencing chronic pain. Currently I'm working to overcome some deep-rooted fears connected to my limited mobility. The unfortunate reality is that this could possibly be my last decade to be able to move. The steady decline in the use of my arms over the past three years has led me to accept my body in a whole new way. I'm learning to love myself as I am, even in this broken body.

One of my greatest challenges has been embracing self-worth, finding purpose in this endless suffering and trying to shake the feeling of being a burden. When you're rendered absolutely helpless and can't even reach your hands up to touch your own face, there are so many big emotions to balance. I often feel like a toddler as I must be showered, dressed and cared for every single day.

During my recent recovery from my fourth joint replacement, I didn't know if I'd make it through. I sunk so low, so deep, aided by all the crazy pain meds I was on, I even told my husband that he should get rid of me. The thoughts of, "If I was a horse, they'd shoot me!" haunted me as I saw myself making it easier on him if I could just cease to exist somehow. Through this process, I became the most unloveable version of myself and yet he chose to love me, cry with me, scream and curse with me. Together we descended into the pit only to later climb out and see how much that we truly love each other. Through this process I've discovered how much I am worthy of love despite my affliction.

As I wrestle daily with this wretched disease that literally eats up my joints, I have pain everywhere. It doesn't matter if I'm moving or lying still, it's there wearing on me, exhausting me, threatening to become the veil through which I live and see myself through.

Knowing that my fifth joint replacement will be scheduled within the next couple of months, it can feel like my life has peaked and I'm now going downhill at the age of forty-one.

Last year I endured the replacement of my left shoulder. As I sit here now, I'm still recovering from the replacement of my left elbow. And with the replacement of my right elbow coming up within the next couple of months, it feels very overwhelming. I've felt buried alive by these circumstances, by not being able to care for my own family, hurting myself in my attempts to do so anyway, damaging my body further, and not valuing myself enough to stop when I know I should.

It's hard to face your fears concerning what's going on in your body when you have severe health issues and chronic pain. When I have the hardest moments, when I can't walk and find myself only limping around to get by, when the pain level is at a nine, when it's been one of those days and I've given it my all, I can still find something to be thankful for. Doing so completely shifts my perspective. I'm thankful that I still have legs and am able to walk. I'm thankful for the fact that I can enjoy how good it feels to put my feet up at the end of the day.

Practicing gratitude is the one thing that always catches me from descending into the pit of despair. There's always someone going through something worse, someone going through something that I could never, ever imagine. It stops me and gives me renewed perspective, causing me to feel grateful for my own situation.

It's amazing how we can be absolutely paralyzed by the fear attached to our circumstances and then quickly set free in that moment when truth and gratitude enter in. As I focus on all that I have to be thankful for, on what I can do instead of what I can't do, my fears are stripped away and I am free to adapt, to laugh, and even to dance in my own funny way.

Leslie

. . .

I was enjoying just a regular quiet evening at home with my family in July of 2016. While watching a movie with my husband and three kids, I discovered something that would soon turn my whole world upside-down. It was a suspicious lump that turned out to be breast cancer.

My mom had breast cancer ten years earlier, so I knew a little about the road that was ahead of me.

On September 19, 2016, I received my official diagnosis. I was absolutely scared. My children were ages seven, eleven, and fourteen at the time. All I could manage to say was, "God, I really want to be there when they graduate high school, when they get married, when they have kids. I want to grow old with my husband." I knew that I had to be strong not only for myself, but for my family. A friend sent me a plaque that said, "Be still and know that I am God." And that's what I did. I put my trust in God.

I chose to do a double mastectomy with reconstruction followed by six rounds of chemo and thirty-one rounds of radiation. My surgery was on October 10, 2016 followed by six weeks of recovery. Surgery revealed I was stage 3A with five infected lymph nodes out of the nine that were removed.

God brought so many new friends into my life during that time, it was amazing! They still continue to be some of my closest friends. I got through the holidays and chemo rounds with a voracious appetite. I never once suffered from any nausea, which is very rare considering the intensity of the chemo I was receiving.

Throughout my entire cancer journey, I stayed upbeat and didn't let cancer depress me. I knew in my heart that, through my strong faith and with family and friends surrounding me in prayer, I would get through all of the treatments and surgeries—and I did! It has now been over a year since I was diagnosed. My blood tests have ALL come back normal. My hair is growing back and I have the energy to workout almost every day!

Prior to my diagnosis, I was an active fitness coach. While my illness did limit me to a great degree at times, I stayed as active as possible—even if it was only a short walk on the treadmill a few times a week. Staying active helped me to feel a little more normal, a little more in control of my life, and it also helped me to stay positive. More than anything, physical activity balanced with restful quiet times and also time with friends helped me the most.

Going through my cancer battle, I cried often but I never felt sorry for myself or blamed God. I *fought* and I *fought hard!* My goal the entire time was to get through by leaning completely on my faith in God's ability to carry me. I couldn't have done as well as I did through everything that year if it wasn't for my faith and my community of family and friends.

I'm grateful to be on the other side of my storm, happily living life with my family, and getting to see my children grow up. I'm back to working part-time in the world of fitness at our local YMCA. I don't know what the future holds, but I cling to one of my favorite verses:

• • •

"For I know the plans I have for you, says
the Lord. They are plans for good and not for evil,
to give you a future and a hope."

JEREMIAH 29:11 (TLB)

Michele

...

The day my husband was diagnosed with cholangiocarcinoma, a rare and deadly cancer of the bile ducts, the world we knew ended. A whole new world was opened up to us—the world of discovering natural cancer healing cures through nutrition. We learned how to upgrade our lifestyle from the typical Standard American Diet (SAD), to a nutritious, delicious, and life-saving plant-based diet. We went vegan, something no one ever would have believed. Our family was shocked. WE were shocked.

A cancer diagnosis plunges you into the dark pit of fear, despair, and hopelessness. Who survives cancer these days? Through traditional chemotherapy methods, radiation and surgery, some lives may be prolonged. However, in too many cases the cancer resurfaces after a period of remission and takes the person out quickly.

The day after my husband's cancer diagnosis, I went on record with God. I told Him that I had never been so afraid. My fear was founded in the fact that I had prayed for many people with cancer through the years, but not one had survived. I had never witnessed a single healing. Not one. I had heard of miracles for other people, but all the loved ones I prayed for had passed. I was devastated.

In spite of my fear, I chose to anchor my heart in the fact that I KNEW God loved me. God had brought my family and me through many crises over the years through prayer, trust, and His abundant grace. I trusted that His plan for me—for us—was for victory and life, no matter what was about to happen.

I prayed that day like never before that I would trust in God no matter the outcome, even if it was time for my beloved husband of thirty-nine years to go to Heaven sooner than I thought he should. I chose to lean into my faith regarding this life-threatening illness.

I believe in the healing power of God and I believe there are specific things we need to do to facilitate healing and thriving in our lives.

We need to participate with the process. We need to choose life and health. We need to surround ourselves with the positive. Find those testimonies of people who have overcome sorrowful circumstances by choosing life and seeking joyful expression. Every life circumstance is an opportunity to grow and learn how to overcome and thrive while traversing this complex human experience on planet earth.

I have good news! Thanks to a combination of surgery, a plant-based diet, and divine intervention, Mike is now cancer-free and together we are thriving! His healing journey through nutrition taught me many things. Because of my newfound passion for natural healing, I became a Certified Nutritional Health Coach through the Institute for Integrative Nutrition.

The book of our healing journey, *Body Speak: Listen to your Body it Knows What it's Talking About!* is now available at *amazon.com* (written by me, Michele Rizzo).

Rachel

...

I had the fairy tale marriage to the man of my dreams, the kind of guy that most girls might dream of.

Stewart and I were absolutely in love and fully enjoyed our adventure-filled life together. Since the very beginning, we shared a dream of building a log cabin in the woods. It would be our dream home in Alabama, one that we would build completely from scratch using only our own four hands.

After several years spent planning, gathering tools, and waiting on God's timing, we at last acquired the logs for our project in 2009. It was such an amazing time of our dreams coming to fruition as many friends and family members came alongside us in support of our crazy adventure. We spent our days hand peeling the logs for our cabin and life was good. We were even trying to start our family together.

All of that suddenly changed on April 17, 2010 when my world totally fell apart. While backwards barefoot waterskiing with his ski team that morning, Stewart suffered a fatal collision and was tragically killed right before my very eyes. I honestly didn't think I would survive it. There were many days I thought my heart would just stop beating, it was working so hard to pump blood to my body. I was utterly devastated.

About a month after the accident, I felt strongly compelled to get back out to the cabin. Two days prior to Stewart's death, we had installed some windows and I wanted to paint them. It was a big deal going back out there, but God's strength, peace, and grace were so evidently covering me.

A few months later, I began to feel the need to finish that cabin, to complete what my husband and I had started. That was an absolutely overwhelming notion. How could I do this without Stewart? But my dad, who was a huge support for me at the time, encouraged me with some words I'll never forget. "How do you eat an elephant? One bite at a time."

He was right, and that became my motto for life. There were so many things I had to do that were so hard and overwhelming that I didn't feel like I could do them. But by God's grace and the encouraging support of family and friends, I chose to attack things "one bite at a time." I spent the next three years of my life chipping away on the project, going to classes to learn certain techniques so I could use them in the cabin. I met all sorts of awesome people that God put in my path to help me along the way.

Pouring myself into the building and finishing of the cabin was an outlet of creativity as well as a place for me to pour out my pain. It allowed me to keep my hands busy while my mind and heart grappled with my new reality. My blood, sweat, and tears literally became a part of the project. The cabin came to represent the rebuilding of my very heart. In the end, I did every last thing that I set my will to do, including finishing the log cabin.

Upon completion of the project, I decided that I needed some time away to clear my head. I followed a desire in my heart and moved out west to do something totally different for a while. In the meantime, some friends rented out the cabin and transformed it into a cozy home. I visited for a week in the summer and had the most wild experience sleeping on the porch of my very own cabin in the woods, only this time as a guest.

In 2015, I began to feel a nudge to return to my log home. I had a strong sense that I needed to go to the cabin to deal with some unfinished business in my heart. This was the sort of thing that could only be dealt with by returning, facing my pain, and allowing God to heal the deepest parts of me. And so I did.

I am now living in the cabin that I built. It is so beautiful and carries such a spirit of Peace. God's presence truly resides here and it has become such a place of rest and restoration for me. I am now taking steps to prepare my log home to be a place for others to receive restoration and healing.

This deep journey has been one of pain and ashes, exploration and discovery. I am now starting to see beauty that has been woven through it all like a golden thread. We may not understand why God allows certain things to happen, but we can trust Him. He has a beautiful tapestry that He is weaving for a purpose that is way bigger than us.

At the end of a painful journey, our lives are much richer, deeper, more compassionate, and more able to experience the depths of God. I'm now more able to offer all of that to others than I would have been had I never experienced the pain of devastating loss. Although I wouldn't have chosen to go through what I have, I am very thankful for all I have gained in the process.

Tenessa

• • •

I have spent most of my life chasing the hope that my mother would someday love me.

She is mother to six children, yet mom to just one. What, might you ask, is my measure of a mom? Unconditional love, acceptance, care, loyalty, affection, and trust are just a few of the qualities I have never experienced with the woman that I have, at times, begged to be my mom.

It is so painful to not have a place to fail safely and know that someone will carefully return you to your true self. To have to perform for a mother's love is exhausting and left me only feeling empty, hopeless, and lonely. I remember thinking that surely she would love me "this time". Surely she will be there and defend me "this time". But she didn't choose to protect me or defend me. The acceptance of that sad reality was too painful, so I just kept giving her the opportunity to love me.

When I was fifteen years old, my parents divorced and a deep depression set in. By the time I was in my early twenties, I had been hospitalized twice with clinical depression. I needed my mom most at this time and she was unavailable. It was very difficult for me to accept that my mother would never be my mom because she was mothering my brother—why not me?

My expectation of my mother's affection was always met with disappointment. The unjust attacks aimed at me from her or the outright neglect and rejection caused me to feel like I was being suffocated by pain. I couldn't understand it or fix it. My only defense against the pain was to take the emotional betrayal and intellectualize it in an attempt to solve it. My deep personal convictions said I would never repay evil with evil—I knew better. You treat people the way you want to be treated; surely that example would draw her closer.

Unfortunately, this unhealthy pattern would only continue in my future relationships and, finally, in an unfaithful spouse. I relied heavily on the logic that if I was kind and loving to them, they would be kind and loving to me. I gave them space in my heart that I had carefully sectioned off and constructed for "Mom", "Dad", "Best Friend", "Husband". When they blew up those rooms, instead of changing the space, I would carefully come back and do the work to reconstruct their spaces and make them beautiful in my eyes.

I patiently waited for when they wanted to come back and, again and again, they came in and blew it up. I was "overcoming", "restoring", "forgiving", all the great attributes my faith professed. I trusted that my faithful diligence would change the outcome.

What I wasn't doing, however, was creating healthy boundaries. I had never learned or experienced boundaries in a healthy way. In my mind, to let go meant to reject someone, to limit was to be selfish, and to deny access was to be inauthentic. My high school quote was, "To see me is to hate me and to know me is to love me." I let everyone in that wanted in because I so desperately wanted to be loved. The illusion of companionship was more bearable than the reality of abandonment, but a heart without boundaries will never find the safety it desires.

Being brave sometimes means you get hurt. Loss has layers of grief that can take years to process. Knowing what I was losing in letting go of my most significant relationships delayed that process many times. But the Lord is faithful and has walked me through it in stages that allow me to stay true to my affection for them and honor these people that I love deeply—Mom, Dad, ex-husband, etc.

My first step towards creating healthy boundaries was closing the doors to those rooms I had sectioned off for toxic people. I learned to stop letting them into these rooms filled with huge expectations that their history and capacity could never fill. This meant that I no longer had to maintain these rooms or fix them when they were destroyed.

The next step was to create a more realistic space in my heart for who these people were capable of being in my life. That created more realistic expectations and sometimes none at all. Practicing forgiveness enabled me to successfully heal in this place and create these new spaces in my heart.

The third step for me, which has been more recent, has been to no longer have these rooms at all. What I realized was, by giving this much room in my heart for my unavailable mom, I didn't allow myself to be "mothered" by anyone. By creating healthy boundaries, I have a chance to experience love from a healthy individual who can occupy space in my heart because of who they are and not what I wish they would be.

Letting go and creating healthy boundaries for myself helped me stop fighting for and working alone to fix unsolvable problems in toxic relationships. I learned so many coping mechanisms for surviving toxic people, but the Lord wants us thriving—not merely surviving. He led me through the loss and, while I don't have replacements for any of these relationships, I am developing a trust in God and intimacy with Jesus that I have never known before. I am currently the most alone I have ever been and yet I am not lonely. God's companionship is rewriting my history and creating a healthy expectation of love that will bring the relationships I have always dreamed of.

YOUR STORY

...

Thank you for taking this thirty-day journey with me.
I hope that you have been encouraged and inspired to thrive
through whatever storm you may face now or in the future.
While I realize that there may be nothing I could say that will
end your personal storm, we can all support one another and,
together, discover a new healthy balance in life.

I invite you to share your own stories and how this book
has brought you closer to a thriving life by joining the
30 Days to Thriving Readers Community at:

FACEBOOK.COM/GROUPS/30DAYSTOTHRIVING

...

To inquire about health coaching or
to hire Jennifer for your next wellness event, send an
e-mail to ***support@jenniferzimmer.com***

NOTES

. . .

DAY 7: FILTERING THOUGHTS

1. Leaf, Dr. Caroline. 2017. *Toxic Thoughts.* Video. http://drleaf.com/media/toxic-thoughts/

DAY 11: LEARNING TO LAUGH AGAIN

1. Mendoza, Dr. Marilyn A. 2016. "The Healing Power Of Laughter In Death And Grief." *Psychology Today.* https://www.psychologytoday.com/blog/understanding-grief/201611/the-healing-power-laughter-in-death-and-grief.

2. Sinatra, Dr. Stephen. 2014. "The Healing Power Of Laughter | Heart MD Institute - Dr. Stephen Sinatra's Informational Site." *Heart MD Institute - Dr. Stephen Sinatra's Informational Site.* https://heartmdinstitute.com/stress-relief/healing-power-laughter/

DAY 13: JOURNALING

1. Sinatra, Dr. Stephen. 2014. "The Healing Power Of Laughter | Heart MD Institute - Dr. Stephen Sinatra's Informational Site." *Heart MD Institute - Dr. Stephen Sinatra's Informational Site.* https://heartmdinstitute.com/stress-relief/healing-power-laughter/

DAY 18: HELPING OTHERS

1. "Help Others." 2017. *Mental Health America.* Accessed November 5. http://www.mentalhealthamerica.net/help-others

DAY 19: PRIORITIZING YOU

1. Firestone, Dr. Lisa. 2017. "The Unselfish Art Of Prioritizing Yourself." *Psychology Today.* https://www.psychologytoday.com/blog/compassion-matters/201708/the-unselfish-art-prioritizing-yourself

2. Jones, Maryann. 2013. "Prioritize Yourself And Thrive." *Wellness Today.* http://www.wellnesstoday.com/nutrition/prioritize-yourself-and-thrive.

DAY 20: BREATHING DEEPLY

1. Marksberry, Kellie. 2012. "Take A Deep Breath." *The American Institute Of Stress.* https://www.stress.org/take-a-deep-breath/

2. Douillard, Dr. John. 2014. "15 Benefits Of Nose Breathing Exercise | John Douillard's Lifespa." *Dr. Douillard's Lifespa.* https://lifespa.com/15-benefits-nose-breathing-exercise/

3. Preston, Dr. John D. 2017. "The Habits Of Stress-Resilient People." Presentation, Redding, California. 2017

DAY 21: CONNECTING WITH NATURE

1.   Howard, Brian Clark. 2013. "Connecting With Nature Boosts Creativity And Health." *news.nationalgeographic.com.* https://news.nationalgeographic.com/news/2013/06/130628-richard-louv-nature-deficit-disorder-health-environment/

2.   Oschman, James, Gaetan Chevalier, and Richard Brown. 2015. "The Effects Of Grounding (Earthing) On Inflammation, The Immune Response, Wound Healing, And Prevention And Treatment Of Chronic Inflammatory And Autoimmune Diseases." *NCBI.* https://www.ncbi.nlm.nih.gov/pmc/articles/PMC4378297/

DAY 22: PRACTICING AROMATHERAPY

1.   "Aromatherapy Pure, Organic Essential Oils | Aromatics International." 2017. *aromatics.com.* https://www.aromatics.com

DAY 25: EATING FOR LIFE: PART 1 (MACRONUTRIENTS)

1.   Lawrence, Star. 2017. "Food To Balance Your Mood." *Webmd.* Accessed November 5. https://www.webmd.com/food-recipes/features/food-to-balance-your-mood#1

2.   Szalay, Jessie. 2015. "What Is Protein?" *Live Science.* https://www.livescience.com/53044-protein.html

3.   "15 Omega-3 Foods Your Body Needs Now - Dr. Axe." 2017. *Dr. Axe.* Accessed November 5. https://draxe.com/omega-3-foods/

4. "Omega 3 Benefits Plus Top 10 Omega 3 Foods List - Dr. Axe." 2017. *Dr. Axe.* https://draxe.com/omega-3-benefits-plus-top-10-omega-3-foods-list/

DAY 26: EATING FOR LIFE: PART 2 (MICRONUTRIENTS)

1. Gonzalez, MJ, and JR Miranda-Massari. 2014. "Diet And Stress. - Pubmed - NCBI." *ncbi.nlm.nih.gov.* https://www.ncbi.nlm.nih.gov/pubmed/25455067

2. "Facts About Vitamin C And Adrenal Fatigue." 2017. Adrenal Fatigue Recovery. Accessed November 6. http://www.adrenalfatiguerecovery.com/vitamin-c.html.

3. "Vitamin C Foods, Signs Of Deficiency & Health Benefits." 2017. *Dr. Axe.* Accessed November 5. https://draxe.com/vitamin-c-foods/

4. Kaplan, Bonnie J., Julia J. Rucklidge, Amy R. Romijn, and Michael Dolph. 2015. "A Randomised Trial Of Nutrient Supplements To Minimise Psychological Stress After A Natural Disaster." *Psychiatry Research.* http://www.psy-journal.com/article/S0165-1781(15)00393-5/abstract

5. "Vitamin B12 Benefits And Deficiency Symptoms - Dr. Axe." 2017. *Dr. Axe.* Accessed November 5. https://draxe.com/vitamin-b12-benefits/

6. Kresser, Chris. 2012. "The Little Known (But Crucial) Difference Between Folate And Folic Acid." *Chris Kresser.* https://chriskresser.com/folate-vs-folic-acid/

7.   Patel, Arti. 2015. "13 Foods Full Of Vitamin B." *Huffpost Canada*. http://www.huffingtonpost.ca/entry/vitamin-b-foods_n_6672018.html

8.   Zelman, Kathleen M. 2017. "The Risks Of Excess Vitamins And Other Nutrients." *Webmd*. Accessed November 5. https://www.webmd.com/vitamins-and-supplements/nutrition-vitamins-11/fat-water-nutrient

9.   "Are You Vitamin D Deficient? - draxe.com." 2017. *Dr. Axe*. Accessed November 5. https://draxe.com/vitamin-d-deficiency/

10. "3 Things Everyone Should Know About Vitamin D - Dr. Axe." 2017. *Dr. Axe*. Accessed November 5. https://draxe.com/3-things-everyone-should-know-about-vitamin-d/

11. "These Foods, Herb, Spices & Oils Are Absolutely Bursting With Antioxidants." 2017. *Dr. Axe*. Accessed November 5. https://draxe.com/top-10-high-antioxidant-foods/

DAY 27: BOOSTING GUT HEALTH

1.   Gottfried, Dr. Sara. 2017. "Dysbiosis Decoded: Symptoms & The Why's | Sara Gottfried MD." *saragottfriedmd.com*. Accessed November 5. http://www.saragottfriedmd.com/dysbiosis-symptoms-and-conditions/

2.   Borchard, Therese. 2015. "10 Ways To Cultivate Good Gut Bacteria And Reduce Depression." *everydayhealth.com*. https://www.everydayhealth.com/columns/therese-borchard-sanity-break/ways-cultivate-good-gut-bacteria-reduce-depression

3. Yang, Chun, Yuko Fujita, Qian Ren, Min Ma, Chao Dong, and Kenji Hashimoto. 2017. "Bifidobacterium In The Gut Microbiota Confer Resilience To Chronic Social Defeat Stress In Mice." *NCBI*. https://www.ncbi.nlm.nih.gov/pmc/articles/PMC5377462/

DAY 28: SLEEPING WELL

1. Preston, Dr. John D. 2017. "The Habits Of Stress-Resilient People." Presentation, Redding, California. 2017.

2. "Sleep.org By The National Sleep Foundation." 2017. *sleep.org*. Accessed November 5. https://sleep.org/articles/sleep-better-when-stressed/

DAY 30: BOUNCING FORWARD

1. Sandberg, Sheryl; Grant. 2017. *Option B*. [S.l.]: Knopf Doubleday Publishing Group.

2. Johnson, Season. 2017. *Kickcancer*. Accessed November 5. https://kickcancermovement.org

STAY CONNECTED

• • •

FACEBOOK

ThriveHolisticHealthCoaching

INSTAGRAM

@thriveholistichealth

TWITTER

@coach2thrive

• • •

Stay connected to learn more about upcoming
health coaching programs such as my 3-month Mindset
Makeover, speaking events and workshops.

DID YOU ENJOY THIS BOOK?

Please write a review and leave your
honest feedback on Amazon!

TRY HEALTH COACHING!

. . .

This book was inspired by my experience at the Institute for Integrative Nutrition® (IIN), where I received my training in holistic wellness and health coaching.

IIN offers a truly comprehensive Health Coach Training Program that invites students to deeply explore the things that are most nourishing to them. From the physical aspects of nutrition and eating wholesome foods that work best for each individual person, to the concept of Primary Food discussed in this book, IIN helped me reach optimal health and balance. This journey unleashed the passion that compels me to share what I've learned and inspire others.

IIN leads people like you and me step-by-step through the process of launching successful health coaching careers, offering training in coaching techniques, business management and marketing strategies. Students who choose to pursue this field professionally will complete the program equipped with the communication skills and branding knowledge they need to create a fulfilling career encouraging and supporting others in reaching their own health goals.

This school has changed my life and I believe it can do the same for you. I invite you to learn more about the Institute for Integrative Nutrition and explore how the Health Coach Training Program can help you transform your life. Feel free to contact me to hear more about my personal experience at *jenniferzimmer.com/health-coaching*, or call 844-315-8546 to learn more.

94035093R00163

Made in the USA
Columbia, SC
18 April 2018